A TREASURY OF

Gilbert & Sullivan

The Words and the Music of One Hundred and Two Songs from
Eleven Operettas • Edited by DEEMS TAYLOR • Illustrated by
LUCILLE CORCOS • Arrangements by DR. ALBERT SIRMAY

SIMON AND SCHUSTER • NEW YORK • 1941

MANUFACTURED IN THE UNITED STATES OF AMERICA
PRINTED BY REEHL LITHO
AND BOUND BY H. WOLFF, NEW YORK

CONTENTS

INTRODUCTION

YOU NEVER KNOW. Arthur Seymour Sullivan, in his day, was the unofficial composer laureate of England. At the age of thirteen, he had seen his first published composition, an anthem, *O Israel*, in print. At twenty, his incidental music to *The Tempest* made him famous, like Byron, practically overnight. At twenty-two, he was hearing a commissioned cantata, *Kenilworth*, sung at the Birmingham Festival. Two years later, his *In Memoriam* Overture put him in the first rank of contemporary British composers. After that, an increasingly important career as a serious composer: more cantatas—*The Prodigal Son, On Shore and Sea, The Light of the World, The Martyr of Antioch, The Golden Legend*; more Shakespeare music—*The Merchant of Venice, The Merry Wives of Windsor, Henry VIII, Macbeth*; songs and hymns by the dozen; knighthood at forty-one, "in recognition of your distinguished talents as a composer and of the services which you have rendered to the promotion of the art of music generally in this country"; a grand opera, *Ivanhoe*. What better insurance of immortality could any composer ask?

Then there was William Schwenck Gilbert, who, starting with a burlesque, *Dr. Dulcamara*, produced when he was thirty, diligently pursued a career as a writer of plays—*The Wicked World, Sweethearts, Engaged*, and a dozen others.

And what is left of Sullivan, the "serious" composer? Practically speaking, one hymn, *Onward, Christian Soldiers*, and a song, *The Lost Chord*. The rest? Museum pieces. And of Gilbert, the dramatist? The amateur dramatic societies still perform *Engaged*, on occasion. The rest is silence.

What was really significant in the careers of the two men (and neither would ever have believed it) was a highly unsuccessful operetta, produced in 1871, for which Gilbert had written the libretto and for which Sullivan had been persuaded to compose the music. The piece was not even published, but it turned out to be the first of a series of fourteen, eleven of which, at least, have served to make the trade-mark, "Gilbert and Sullivan," as nearly immortal as any two names in the history of operetta can hope to be.

The "and" in Gilbert and Sullivan is important; for it is what made the whole greater than the sum of the parts. Gilbert as a playwright, without Sullivan, was a prolific writer of farces, a few of which are still faintly amusing, and of pompous Victorian dramas, none of which was particularly successful even in its day, and all of which are, by contemporary standards, terrible. Sullivan, without Gilbert, was the creator of a mass of "serious" music which was, at its best, highly watered Mendelssohn. It is not surprising that an England whose musical god was Mendelssohn should have been enthusiastic over his English disciple. Still less is it surprising that the setting of Mendelssohn's sun should have coincided with the disappearance of the Sullivan of *Ivanhoe* and *The Light of the World*.

But the two as a team—ah, that is a different matter. Gilbert was fatally handicapped as a serious dramatist by the heavy veil of Victorian moralism that made it impossible for him to look at any phase of human conduct with completely clear vision. As a librettist, he need not be concerned with the moralities, since

[7]

the creatures of the Savoy operettas were never by any chance real people. He had a chance to give free rein to the mordant wit that was one of his greatest gifts. Above all, he had an ideal medium, in the lyrics, for his genius for rhyme and rhythm, particularly so as he had for a collaborator one of the few English-speaking composers who have ever shown signs of understanding the quantities and accents of the English language.

Sullivan was equally lucky, in that Gilbert freed him from the responsibility of being England's un-official composer laureate, a position that, away from Gilbert, he took with calamitous seriousness. Compos-ing the Savoy operettas, he was under no obligation to set lofty sentiments to music, or to convey—try, at least, to convey—any weighty musical message. All he had to do was to relax, mentally and spiritually, and, given Gilbert's enchanting lyrics, indulge to the fullest his one treasurable gift, that of creating simple, sparkling, *vocal* melodies. Between them, the two managed to produce a series of small satiric master-pieces that have long outlived the objects of their satire.

Just now I emphasized the vocal quality of Sullivan's airs. His own methods of work still further emphasize that quality. He described them to Arthur Lawrence, his official biographer, as follows:*

"The first thing I have to decide upon is the rhythm, and I arrange the rhythm before I come to the question of melody." (At that point in the interview with Law-rence he wrote out eight different metrical settings of the song, "Were I Thy Bride," from *The Yeomen of the Guard*.) "You see that seven out of eight methods were commonplace, and my first aim has always been to get as much originality as possible in the rhythm, approaching the question of melody afterwards. . . . My first work, the jotting down of the melodies, I term 'sketches.' They are hieroglyphics which, possibly, would seem undecipherable. It is my musical short-hand, and, of course, it means much to me. When I have finished these sketches the creative part of my work is completed (no talk of harmony, you notice). After that comes the orchestration, which is, of course, a very essential part of the work, and entails some severe manual labor.

"When the 'sketch' is completed, which means writ-ing, rewriting, and alterations of every description, the work is drawn out in so-called 'skeleton score,' that is, with all the vocal parts, rests for symphonies,† etc., completed, but without a note of the accompani-

ment or instrumental work of any kind, although, naturally, I have all that in mind. Then the voice parts are written out by the copyist, and the rehearsals begin. On these occasions I vamp an accompaniment, or, in my absence, the accompanist of the theatre does so. It is not until the music has been thoroughly learnt, and the rehearsals on the stage, with the necessary action and 'business,' are well advanced, that I begin the orchestration. . . . Meanwhile the full score has been taken in hand, and from it an accompaniment for the voice parts has been 'reduced' for the piano, so that the 'words and music' is ready for the public simu-laneously with the production."

Which brings us to Doctor Sirmay's piano arrange-ments for the present volume. As you will see from the above account, Sullivan never bothered with written piano parts at rehearsals and took no part in making even the published piano versions. This work was done by some hack arranger whose chief preoccupation was to turn out a piano score whose execution would not be beyond the technical powers of a young lady of the eighties who had "taken" piano for a year or so. The result, as a rule, was an appallingly commonplace series of "VM-pom-pom-pom," bass-and-chord accom-paniments, usually with the tune only in the voice part, which, except that they followed Sullivan's harmoniza-tion, bore no relation to his orchestration. Doctor Sir-may, taking Sullivan's melodies and harmony as a basis, has produced a series of genuine *piano* tran-scriptions. They are not difficult—even that Victorian young lady could play them, if she practiced a bit—but they do give the player and his listeners some idea of the actual effect of the songs. If there are better Gilbert-and-Sullivan piano arrangements, I have not seen them.

In the pages that follow you will find, for every operetta, first, one of Miss Corcos' drawings, just to get you into the spirit of the occasion (and I wish Gil-bert could see them. He would have appreciated them); next, a foreword, which, together with those that pre-cede and follow it, will give you a reasonably ample running account of the progress of that joint career which has entertained so many millions; third, a synop-sis of the plot, which shows where, in the story, the various songs and ensemble numbers occur; and lastly, Doctor Sirmay's transcriptions of Sullivan's music,

---

* *Sir Arthur Sullivan; Life Story, Letters, and Reminiscences*, by Arthur Lawrence. Herbert S. Stone and Company, Chicago and New York, 1900.

† We call them interludes.

together with Gilbert's lyrics. Of the two hundred-odd songs and choruses of which the Gilbert-and-Sullivan repertory boasts you will find more than one hundred. They are, we think, the cream of the collection. No songs from *Thespis, Utopia, Limited,* or *The Grand Duke* are included; the first, because the score no longer exists, the other two, because neither contains any songs that ever achieved real popularity, or that were not reflections of something that the authors had done better before. To include any of them, merely for the sake of the record, would have meant omitting a corresponding number that you would far rather hear. Most of those latter, we believe, you will find in these pages.

DEEMS TAYLOR

A NOTE ABOUT THE PIANO ARRANGEMENTS

THE PIANO ARRANGEMENTS contained in this volume are completely new. I derived them exclusively from the original piano scores, published in London during the composer's lifetime. I also found great help by listening to the recordings of the D'Oyly Carte Opera Company, considered the most dependable custodian of the Gilbert-and-Sullivan tradition.

In making these new arrangements, my guiding principle was the strict and faithful observance of Sullivan's style and spirit. Not once have I touched or altered a single harmony of the composer. It would have been, in my opinion, an anachronistic and unstylish sacrilege to "modernize" the crystal-clear purity of Sullivan's conception.

My only aim was to make all these songs playable and enjoyable to the great mass of Sullivan admirers who possess average pianistic technique. As Mr. Deems Taylor so expertly explains above, Sullivan's piano scores were very superficially offered to the public. The melody appeared only in the voice line and was (with rare exceptions) almost completely banished from the piano part. Dynamic marks and phrasing were fragmentary or entirely missing.

I made it my task to integrate the melody with the piano parts. All ensemble parts were condensed into one vocal line. The only deviation from this rule occurs in a number of *Ruddigore* (THERE GREW A LITTLE FLOWER) where a charming countermelody, which could not be entirely omitted, needed an additional voice line. I found it advisable to substitute English terminology for the monotonously simple and mostly nondescriptive Italian indications for mood and tempo as used in Sullivan's published scores. Within reasonable limits I also added dynamic marks and did not neglect the phrasing of the melodies.

In order to bring the songs within the range of the average voice, I had to transpose more than a third of them into a practical key. All the introductions and postludes are from the original score. In a very few cases the extreme length of choral numbers necessitated the careful and respectful omission of a number of bars, but I have religiously abstained from violating Sullivan's music even by adding one single note which is not his own.

In spite of all my endeavor to simplify the songs pianistically, a few of them remain not quite easy to play, as, for instance, the opening chorus of *The Mikado* (IF YOU WANT TO KNOW). Sullivan was not a "piano composer," in the sense of the word, as were, for instance, Puccini and George Gershwin. These two worked at the piano and consequently wrote excellently for the piano. Sullivan visualized everything orchestrally. His spirited string or woodwind figures often become very hard by being transcribed for the piano keyboard.

May I be allowed to close with a personal note in the nature of a candid confession: the months of work spent on this volume converted me from a complacent listener into a fervent admirer of Sullivan's genius.

ALBERT SIRMAY

TRIAL BY JURY

TRIAL BY JURY

THOMAS GERMAN REED'S Gallery of Illustration would be called a burlesque house today—which would not be entirely correct. It did house an entertainment consisting largely of one-act musical sketches in the manner of the then-popular French "vaudeville"; but the mere fact that Reed had to sidestep the horrid word "theater" in naming it should be a reassurance as to the propriety of what went on within its walls. The Londoner of 1869 would run, screaming, from a modern burlesque show—or at least his wife would.

The Gallery is mentioned here because it was the place of the first meeting between William S. Gilbert and Arthur S. Sullivan, a meeting that was as flatly undramatic as it was eventually important. Reed was rehearsing a musical piece called *Ages Ago,* words by Gilbert, music by Frederick Clay; and Sullivan had asked to meet the librettist.

Young Mr. Sullivan, at twenty-seven, had already become the musical white hope of England. His incidental music to Shakespeare's *The Tempest* had made him a marked man; and his songs and cantatas, and his *In Memoriam* Overture in particular, had established his reputation. However, even then he had given evidence that his talents were not confined to serious music. In 1866 he had written *Cox and Box,* a one-act musical farce to words by F. C. Burnand, for a group of amateurs. It went so well that it was later produced publicly, at a benefit, in '67. Reed, who heard it, had promptly commissioned the two authors to write another, for professional production. The result of the commission, *The Contrabandista,* was put on in December of 1867, at St. George's Hall (no, not "theater"), and ran for three months. Following this, Reed produced *Cox and Box,* which ran for nearly a year. In fact, Gilbert and Sullivan had been on a double bill together some time before they ever met; for in March, 1869, Reed had presented a program consisting of *Cox and Box* and *No Cards,* the latter by Gilbert, with music by L. Elliot.

It was now November. Sullivan had no ulterior motive in hunting up Gilbert. In Burnand he had a librettist with whom he was perfectly satisfied, in case he should ever feel like doing another operetta—which

seemed unlikely. At the moment he was finishing a new cantata, *The Prodigal Son,* for the forthcoming Worcester Festival. Gilbert was equally disinterested. His taste in music was hazy; all he wanted was a composer who would set his words without mutilating the rhythm, and this he had in Clay. It was simply a matter of a well-known young composer wanting to meet the author of the *Bab Ballads* that all London was delightedly reading.

"I'm very glad to meet you, Mr. Sullivan," said Gilbert, "for you will be able to decide a question which has just arisen between my friend Fred Clay and myself." Whereupon he launched into a long and frightfully involved problem in harmonic technique which he had cribbed out of *The Encyclopædia Britannica.* Sullivan, who was not used to being kidded, explained that he couldn't decide the question offhand and went away, promising to think it over.

And that was that. Not for two years did the two meet again, this time professionally. In 1871 Gilbert submitted a libretto to John Hollingshead, manager of the Gaiety Theatre. Hollingshead liked it and took it, in turn, to Sullivan, whom he asked to write the music for it. Sullivan accepted, and the fruits of the collaboration, *Thespis; or, The Gods Grown Old,* had its first performance during the Christmas season of 1871.

This, the first of the Gilbert and Sullivan operettas, was not a very promising start for the famous partnership. The idea, that of a troupe of actors stranded on Mount Olympus, was a good one—at least on paper— but the audiences didn't warm to it. The piece ran for about a month. Popular as Sullivan was, the score was not even published.

Another four years went by. Sullivan traveled in Europe, wrote a Festival *Te Deum* to celebrate the recovery of the Prince of Wales (later Edward VII) from typhoid fever, conducted the "Classical Nights" at the Covent Garden promenade concerts, took over the editorship of *The Hymnal* (for which he wrote *Onward, Christian Soldiers!*), and wrote an oratorio, *The Light of the World,* for the Birmingham Festival. Gilbert wrote six plays, including *The Happy Land,* which had a 200-night run, and *Sweethearts.* Also, on the advice of a friend, he somewhat elaborated a miniature burlesque opera, called *Trial by Jury,* which he had published, in 1868, in the magazine *Fun*. He submitted it to Carl Rosa, the producer, who undertook to write the music himself and produce it as a vehicle for his wife, Madame Parepa-Rosa. She died, however, before the score was begun, and her widower returned the manuscript to its author.

Then another player came upon the scene. He had begun as a composer of light opera, became a theatrical agent, and wound up by being the manager of the Royalty Theatre. Thanks to his combination of ingratiating manners and shrewd business sense, he was known by some members of the profession as "Oily Carte." But Richard D'Oyly Carte was also an uncommonly sound picker of latent talent. Notwithstanding the failure of *Thespis*, he had an idea that Gilbert and Sullivan had in them the makings of a highly successful team; and needing a curtain raiser to go with Offenbach's *La Périchole*, which was running at the Royalty, he asked Gilbert to write him something. The latter promptly produced his revamped *Trial by Jury* text. Carte liked it and suggested that Gilbert get Sullivan to write the music. Here is the story of that meeting, as told by Sullivan to Arthur Lawrence, his biographer:

"It was on a very cold morning, with the snow falling heavily, that Gilbert came round to my place, clad in a heavy fur coat. He had called to read over to me the MS of *Trial by Jury*. He read it through, and, it seemed to me, in a perturbed sort of way, with a gradual crescendo of indignation, in the manner of a man considerably disappointed with what he had written. As soon as he had come to the last word he closed up the manuscript violently, apparently unconscious of the fact that he had achieved his purpose so far as I was concerned, inasmuch as I was screaming with laughter the whole time."

Sullivan wrote the music in three weeks, during which time rehearsals were going on simultaneously. The piece opened—as an afterpiece, by the way, not a curtain raiser—on the evening of March 25, 1875. Sullivan's brother, Fred, who was also in the cast of *La Périchole*, played the role of the Judge. W. S. Penley, from the chorus of the Offenbach piece, was a member of the jury (later, he was promoted to Foreman and, in a part that had only a few lines, scored a resounding personal success). *Trial by Jury* was an instantaneous hit. Within a few weeks all London was whistling its airs and quoting its lyrics. It ran for the rest of the year.

Here was something new: a satire on one branch of English civilization, written by Englishmen, not a burlesque of somebody else's satire on something foreign. Nothing like it had ever been done in England, and England liked it. So has everyone else, ever since; for law courts seem to be equally fair game in all countries. Incidentally, it is the only Gilbert and Sullivan production that has no spoken dialogue.

THE STORY

In a court of justice, Edwin is being sued by Angelina for breach of promise of marriage. The Usher instructs the jury that "from bias free of every kind" the trial must be tried, adding that they need pay no attention when the ruffianly defendant speaks.

They therefore shake their fists passionately at Edwin when he enters and attempts to explain that he no longer feels about Angelina as he did WHEN FIRST MY OLD, OLD LOVE I KNEW. The Judge, a self-made man and pretty complacent about it, enters and tells the story of his life from the beginning, WHEN I, GOOD FRIENDS, WAS CALL'D TO THE BAR. He is enraptured when beautiful Angelina, the plaintiff, the broken flower, the cheated maid, comes in with her bridesmaids. The note he had sent to one of the bridesmaids he causes to be rerouted to her. She reads it, kisses it passionately, and places it in her bosom. Listening to her counsel's pitiful plea in her behalf, which he delivers WITH A SENSE OF DEEP EMOTION, Angelina is so moved that she falls sobbing into the arms of the Foreman of the jury. While the Usher tries in vain to maintain silence in the court, the gallant jurors heap imprecations on Edwin and call for substantial damages.

In vain Edwin begs, OH, GENTLEMEN, LISTEN, I pray, and pleads with them not to bring a young fellow to sorrow, who loves this young lady today and loves that young lady tomorrow. But the plaintiff's counsel, upon referring to a lawbook, discovers that

In the reign of James the Second,
It was generally reckoned
As a very serious crime
To marry two wives at one time.

And while Angelina embraces Edwin, maintaining that she loves him with fervor unceasing, Edwin repels her energetically, protesting that he is a terrible bully, a sot, and a ruffian. All is confusion—until the Judge can stand it no more. He bids the lawyers put their briefs upon the shelf; he will marry her, himself.

When First My Old, Old Love I Knew

Animated

mf

p DEFENDANT

1. When first my old, old love I knew, My
2. (But) joy in-ces-sant palls the sense, And

p

bos-om well'd with joy; My rich-es at her feet I threw,
love, un-chang'd, will cloy; And she be-came a bore in-tense

poco cresc.

I was a love-sick boy! No terms seem'd too ex-trav-a-gant Up-
Un-to her love-sick boy! With fit-ful glim-mer burnt my flame, And

poco cresc.

When I, Good Friends, Was Call'd to the Bar

In spirited tempo

JUDGE

1. When I, good friends, was call'd to the bar, I'd an ap-pe-tite fresh and
2. In West-min-ster Hall I danced a dance, Like a sem-i-de-spond-ent
3. The rich at-tor-ney, he jumped with joy And re-plied to my fond pro-

heart - y, But I was, as man-y young bar-ris-ters are, An
fu - ry; For I thought I nev-er should hit on a chance Of ad-
fes - sions: "You shall reap the re-ward of your pluck, my boy, At the

im - pe - cu - ni - ous par - ty. I'd a swal-low-tail coat ___ of a
dress - ing a Brit-ish ___ Ju - ry. But I soon got tired of third-class
Bai - ley and Mid-dle-sex Ses - sions. You'll ___ soon get used ___ to her

beau-ti-ful blue, A___ brief which I bought of a boo-by, A
jour-neys, And___ din-ners of bread and___ wa-ter, So I
looks," said he, "And a ver-y nice girl___ you'll find her! She may

cou-ple of shirts and a col-lar or two, And a ring___ that look'd like a
fell in love with a rich at-tor-ney's El-der-ly, ug-ly
ver-y well pass for for-ty-three, In the dusk,___ with the light be-

CHORUS

ru-by! He'd a cou-ple of shirts and a col-lar or two, And a
daugh-ter. So he fell in love with a rich at-tor-ney's___
hind her!" She may ver-y well pass for for-ty-three, In the

ring that look'd like a ru-by!
El-der-ly, ug-ly daugh-ter.
dusk, with the light be-hind her!

[20]

With a Sense of Deep Emotion

Moderately

COUNSEL

1. With a sense of deep e-mo-tion, I ap-proach this pain-ful case; For I nev-er had a
2. (See my) in-ter-est-ing cli-ent, Vic-tim of a heart-less wile! See the trai-tor, all de-

no-tion That a man could be so base, Or de-ceive a girl con-
fi-ant, Wear a su-per-cil-ious smile! Sweet-ly smil'd my cli-ent

CHORUS

fid-ing, Vows, et-ce-te-ra, de-rid-ing. He de-ceiv'd a girl con-
on him, Coy-ly woo'd-and- gent-ly won him. Sweet-ly smil'd his cli-ent

Oh, Gentlemen, Listen

Moderately bright

DEFENDANT

1. Oh, gen-tle-men, lis-ten, I pray, Tho' I own that my heart has been
2. (You) can-not eat break-fast all day,— Nor is it the act of a

rang-ing,   Of na-ture the laws I o-bey, For na-ture is
sin-ner,   When break-fast is tak-en a-way, To turn his at-

con - stant - ly chang-ing.   The moon in her phas-es is
ten - tion to din-ner;   And it's not in the range of be-

found, The time and the wind and the weath-er, The
lief, To look up-on him as a glut-ton, Who,

months in suc-ces-sion come round, And you don't find two Mon-days to-
when he is tir-ed of beef,— De-ter-mines to tack-le the

geth-er. Ah!— Con-sid-er the mor-al, I pray, Nor
mut-ton. Ah!— But this I am will-ing to say, If

bring a young fel-low to sor-row, Who loves this young la-dy to-day And loves that young
it will ap-pease her sor-row, I'll mar-ry this la-dy to-day, And I'll mar-ry the

la-dy to-mor-row! 2. You
oth-er to-   mor-row!

THE SORCERER

THE SORCERER

THE man who turned Gilbert and Sullivan into Gilbertandsullivan was neither Gilbert nor Sullivan, but D'Oyly Carte. After the success of *Trial by Jury* he was more than ever convinced that the pair would be a gold mine for anyone who knew how to handle them properly; and he, he felt, was that one. So, first of all, he got them to promise not to write together for anyone else; that settled, he began to look for backers. They were not easy to find. Almost without exception he got the same answer from every potential "angel" that he visited: there was no future in British operetta. The public wouldn't support it. *Trial by Jury* had been a fluke, and its authors would never be able to repeat. Eventually, however, he did manage to get sufficient backing to float a producing company, with himself as managing director. The backers were himself; Chappell and Metzler, the music publishers; Charles Collard, a piano manufacturer; and Bailey-Generalli—"Water Cart Bailey," as he was called—who had a virtual monopoly of London street sprinkling. The new organization, which Carte called The Comedy Opera Company, leased the Opéra Comique and by the middle of 1877 was ready to do business.

The idea was to produce a series of operettas by British authors and composers, among whom were F. C. Burnand and Alfred Cellier, and James Alberti and Frederick Clay. Gilbert and Sullivan, however, were to furnish the piece that would start the new company on its way.

But, at first, neither Gilbert nor Sullivan was in a particularly co-operative mood. Following *Trial by Jury*, Gilbert had had another operetta produced: *Princess Toto*, with music by his old partner, Frederick Clay. His muse had as yet no notion of settling down in holy wedlock with Sullivan's. Besides, he took himself with extreme seriousness as a playwright and had no intention of confining himself to the musical stage. In the two years that followed *Trial by Jury* he wrote, and saw produced, a serious drama, *Dan'l Druce*, and a farce (it is still played by amateurs), *Engaged*. The latter got him into a lawsuit with one William Muskerry, who claimed that the plot of *Engaged* was stolen from one of his (Gilbert won).

Shortly after, he was the defendant in another suit, brought by an actress named Henrietta Hodson, who claimed that he had blacklisted her among the managers. Gilbert won this suit as well, although public opinion was by no means unanimous in his favor. To the end of his life, Gilbert was always having a row with someone or other. He was decidedly not the prototype of Caspar Milquetoast.

Sullivan, meanwhile, had gone off to Italy on a vacation trip. He returned to England during the early winter of 1875-76, writing songs and filling guest-conductor engagements. His friend, the Duke of Edinburgh, had been urging him to take on the principalship of the newly founded National Training School of Music and he finally consented, signing a contract for six years. Just why he did so is a mystery, for he loathed anything connected with teaching, and spent as little time at the school as he decently could. Long before his contract expired, John Stainer was acting principal, and, when it did expire, he promptly resigned. The school was later reorganized to become the present Royal College of Music.

An honorary degree of Doctor of Music from Cambridge made him even more in demand as guest conductor, and he spent much time traveling from one orchestra to another.

But all these activities were halted by the illness and death of his brother Frederick during the winter of 1876-77. Sullivan was devoted to his family. The death of his father, ten years before, had been a severe blow, and this fresh bereavement left him brokenhearted. Frederick, an architect by profession, had built up such a following among the theatergoing public by his performance of the Judge in *Trial by Jury* that Gilbert was writing a part for him in the forthcoming new piece for The Comedy Opera Company, and it is highly probable that, had he lived, he would have given up architecture for a career on the stage.

Significantly enough, while the death of his father and brother had deeply affected Arthur Sullivan the man, they did not affect the activity of Sullivan the composer. On the contrary, just as his father's death had been the inspiration for his *In Memoriam* Overture, his vigils by his brother's deathbed were the occasion of his composing his perennially popular song,

The Lost Chord. When, in April, 1877, Gilbert sent him the libretto of the new operetta, *The Sorcerer*, Sullivan was ready for him.

Gilbert's experiences in the theater (he had written fifteen plays by the age of twenty-four; he was now forty-one) seem to have inspired him with a holy horror of professional actors. He had very definite ideas of how he wanted his roles played and was determined to see them put into effect. He resolved, therefore, to recruit the new company from the ranks of those whose actual stage experience was slight enough to make them tractable. Accordingly, for his female "heavy" he chose a Mrs. Howard Paul, a touring entertainer (she would probably be called a *diseuse* today). Another choice was Richard Temple, who had had some experience in *opéra bouffe*, but was anything but a veteran.

In making these choices he was encouraged by Sullivan, who displayed a leniency in regard to vocal equipment that was amazing in a composer. But he was right. What he needed—and knew it—were not voices, but *singers who could act*. The wisdom of that point of view is attested by the Savoy Opera Company's success.

Another member was George Grossmith, whose specialty was doing pianologues for semiprivate parties, and who hesitated to join the company because, as he pointed out, if he should fail to make good, he would never again be engaged by the Y.M.C.A. Still another was Rutland Barrington, in the part of Doctor Daly, the Vicar—the part that Gilbert had planned for Fred Sullivan. He had had some experience in playing melodramas and was currently touring with Mrs. Paul. Sullivan accepted him without hearing him sing, which,

as Barrington himself remarks in his autobiography, "perhaps was as well." The members of the chorus were outright amateurs or Royal Academy pupils.

The new Comedy Opera Company made its bow at the Opéra Comique, with *The Sorcerer*, "an entirely original modern comic opera," on the evening of November 17, 1877, with the following cast:

Sir Marmaduke Pointdextre	*John Wellington Wells*
Richard Temple	George Grossmith
Alexis..........George Bentham	*Lady Sangazure*
Dr. Daly..Rutland Barrington	Mrs. Howard Paul
Notary..................Mr. Clifton	*Aline*......................Alice May
Constance......Giulia Warwick	*Mrs. Partlet*......Miss Everard

The reception received by *The Sorcerer* proved that D'Oyly Carte was right. Gilbert and Sullivan were a combination to bring joy to the heart of any producer. Gilbert, too, was right. His cast of semiprofessionals worked together with an enthusiasm and sense of teamwork to which the public responded instantly. Incidentally, there was no further mention of the other author-composer combinations that were supposed to contribute to the repertoire of The Comedy Opera Company. From now on, so far as Carte was concerned, it was Gilbert and Sullivan first and last.

While *The Sorcerer* had no sensational run, compared with the record-breaking ones of some of the subsequent operettas, it was a decided success. Even so, D'Oyly Carte had trouble with his backers, who nagged him to close the show every time the box-office receipts showed signs of slackening. He stood them off, however, until May 22, 1878, when the piece finally closed after a run of 175 performances.

THE STORY

Let's concentrate and get this all straight right away. In the village of Ploverleigh, lovely Aline Sangazure is betrothed to dashing Alexis Pointdextre of the Grenadier Guards. His father, Sir Marmaduke, was of old in love with her mother, Lady Sangazure. Constance Partlet, a village girl, is secretly enamored of Dr. Daly, the Vicar, while her mother, Mrs. Partlet, a Pew-opener, has designs on the Notary. Dr. Daly, although he remembers that TIME WAS, WHEN LOVE AND I were well acquainted, is unaware of Constance's passion. But Aline and Alexis are so thoroughly aware of each other's that they search out the village sorcerer, a businesslike fellow who announces that MY NAME IS JOHN WELLINGTON WELLS, and who, in order to extend the joy of love to all the inhabitants of the village, sells them a love-at-first-sight philter with which they spike the tea at the village picnic. The villagers and the gentry accept their invitations to the feast unsuspectingly, murmuring with joy, NOW TO THE BANQUET WE PRESS.

The love potion works only too well. Sir Marmaduke, Alexis' father, falls in love with humble Mrs. Partlet; Lady Sangazure gives her heart to the sorcerer, Mr. Wells (who happens to be engaged); Constance forgets Dr. Daly and instead returns the affections of the ancient Notary; while, worst of all, Aline Sangazure, having taken the potion at the express wish of Alexis, who feels that it will cement their love forever, happens to catch sight of Dr. Daly just as the potion starts working and falls madly in love with him.

But the heroic John Wellington Wells saves the day. In spite of the fact that his firm of sorcerers is to take inventory on the following week, and he will be badly missed, he breaks the spell by giving his life to the powers of evil. Alexis and Aline are reunited; Dr. Daly and Constance admit their love; Mrs. Partlet goes back to her old flame, the Notary; and Sir Marmaduke Pointdextre is at last accepted by his old and well-descended love, Lady Sangazure.

Time Was, When Love and I

was, when maid-ens of the no-blest sta-tion, For sak-ing ev-en mil-i-ta-ry
care, no jeal-ous doubts hung o'er me, For I was lov'd be-yond all oth-er

cresc. *mf*

men, Would gaze up-on me, rapt in ad-o-ra-tion, Ah
men. Fled gild-ed dukes and belt-ed earls be-fore me, Ah

me, Ah me, I was a fair young cu-rate then!
me, Ah me, I was a pale young cu-rate

then! A pale young cu-rate, a pale young cu-rate, Ah

me, I was a pale young cu-rate then!

My Name Is John Wellington Wells

MR. WELLS

My name is John Well-ing-ton Wells,—— I'm a deal-er in mag-ic and spells,—— In bless-ings and curs-es And ev-er-fill'd purs-es, In proph-e-cies, witch-es, and knells.—— If you want a proud foe to "make tracks"—— If you'd

melt a rich un-cle in wax ___ You've but to look in On the res - i - dent Djinn, Num-ber

sev - en-ty, Sim-mer-y Axe. ___ We've a first-rate as-sort-ment of mag-ic; And for

rais-ing a post-hu-mous shade, With ef-fects that are com-ic or trag-ic, There's

no cheap-er house in the trade. ___ Love-phil-tre, we've quan-ti-ties of it! And for

knowl-edge if an - y-one burns, ___ We're keep-ing a ver-y small proph-et, a proph-et. Who

Mir - rors so mag - i - cal, Facts as - tro - nom - i - cal, Sol - emn or com - i - cal,

And, if you want it, he Makes a re - duc - tion on tak - ing a quan - ti - ty!

cresc.

Oh! _____ If an - y - one an - y - thing lacks, _____ He'll

find it all read - y in stacks, _____ If he'll on - ly look in On the

res - i - dent Djinn, Num - ber sev - en - ty, Sim - mer - y Axe. _____

He can raise you hosts Of ghosts,. And that, with-out re - flec - tors; And creep - y things With wings, And gaunt and gris - ly spec - tres; He can fill you crowds Of shrouds, And hor - ri - fy you vast - ly; He can rack your brains With chains,___ And

quire an a-pol-o-gy! Oh! _____ My name is John Well-ing-ton Wells, ___ I'm a

deal-er in mag-ic and spells, ___ In bless-ings and curs-es, And ev-er fill'd purs-es, In

proph-e-cies, witch-es, and knells. ___ And if an-y-one an-y-thing lacks, ___ He'll

find it all read-y in stacks, ___ If he'll on-ly look in On the res-i-dent Djinn, Num-ber

sev-en-ty, Sim-mer-y Axe!

Now to the Banquet We Press

Light and cheerful

CHORUS

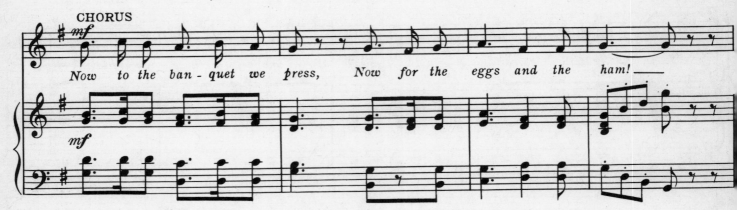

Now to the ban-quet we press, Now for the eggs and the ham!

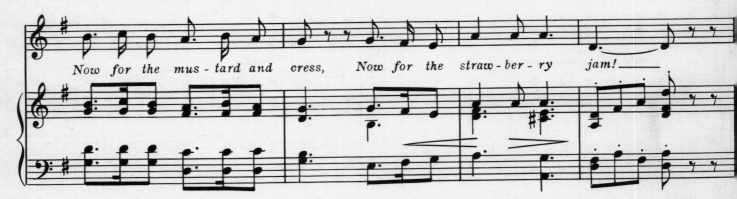

Now for the mus-tard and cress, Now for the straw-ber-ry jam!

Now for the tea of our host! Now for the rol-lick-ing

bun, — Now for the muf - fin and toast, And now for the gay Sal - ly Lunn! — Now for the muf - fin and toast, And now for the gay Sal - ly Lunn! The eggs and the ham And the straw - ber - ry jam, The rol - lick - ing bun And the gay Sal - ly Lunn! The eggs and the ham And the straw - ber - ry jam, The rol - lick - ing bun And the

gay Sal - ly Lunn! The eggs and the ham And the straw - ber - ry jam, And the

rol - lick - ing bun! The rol - lick - ing bun And the gay Sal - ly Lunn And the

straw - ber - ry jam, jam, bun, jam, bun, Oh! the

straw - ber - ry, straw - ber - ry jam, bun, jam, bun, jam, Oh!

the rol - lick - ing, rol - lick - ing bun!

H.M.S. PINAFORE

OR
The Lass That Loved a Sailor

H.M.S. PINAFORE

OR
The Lass That Loved a Sailor

AS SOON as *The Sorcerer* had been successfully launched, Sullivan ran over to Paris for a vacation. Gilbert, on the other hand, was so stimulated that he went immediately to work, to such good effect that by the end of December, 1878, he was able to send his collaborator a new libretto, with a note to say that "I have very little doubt whatever but that you will be pleased with it." And how right he was. No sooner had he read the script, which was entitled, *H.M.S. Pinafore; or, The Lass That Loved a Sailor*, than the excited Sullivan rushed home to begin the music.

The score of *Pinafore*, one of the gayest and catchiest that he ever wrote, is an extraordinary reminder that "mind over matter" is no mere platitude. Ever since his thirtieth year, Sullivan had suffered intermittent torture from a stone in the kidney. He would have longish periods of complete relief, only to be followed by spasmodic attacks of almost continuous pain. This, as Hesketh Pearson, one of his biographers, points out, probably explains his working habits. His composing was almost always done in a fury of energy, generally at the last minute. The work completed and launched, he would spend months, in the country or at some resort, doing nothing at all. Says Pearson, "the presence or near-presence of this disease drove him to work in a frantic effort to forget it; its complete absence was such a relief that he would take advantage of the blessed interregnum and revel in the futilities of social life or dream away the hours in some rural retreat." He started the *Pinafore* music during one of his worst attacks, and his work on it was constantly interrupted by periods of blinding agony.

Gilbert, meanwhile, was rehearsing the book, and Albert Cellier the music, between performances of *The Sorcerer;* and by the time it had ended its run, the new piece was ready to replace it. There were some newcomers in the company. George Power replaced George Bentham as leading tenor; Emma Howson, an American, replaced Mrs. Howard Paul; and Jessie Bond, destined to become the Savoy Company's ingenue lead for years, took the place of Giulia Warwick.

The Sorcerer closed on Wednesday, May 22, 1878. On Saturday evening, the twenty-fifth, The Comedy Opera Company presented *H.M.S. Pinafore; or, The Lass That Loved a Sailor,* "an entirely original nautical comic opera in two acts," with the following cast:

Sir Joseph Porter, K.C.B. George Grossmith	*Bob Becket*..........Mr. Dymott
Captain Corcoran Rutland Barrington	*Tom Tucker*..Mr. Fitzalmont
Ralph Rackstraw George Power	*Sergeant of Marines* Hugh Talbot
Dick Deadeye Richard Temple	*Josephine*......Emma Howson
Bill Bobstay.......Mr. Clifton	*Hebe*...................Jessie Bond
	Mrs. Cripps (*Little Buttercup*) Miss Everard

(The role of Hebe was originally a speaking part, but Jessie Bond, feeling that she had not had enough stage experience to handle spoken lines, persuaded Gilbert to cut them.)

The story of *Pinafore*'s fitful, and eventually triumphant, career has been told so often that it will suffice here merely to summarize it. At first it was definitely not a success. Even the fact that Sir Joseph was a frank caricature of Sir William H. Smith, a publisher whom Queen Victoria had just appointed First Lord of the Admiralty (he made a very good one, by the way), failed to arouse enough curiosity to fill the house. Furthermore, there was a prolonged hot spell that June, and the more solvent Londoners took refuge in the country. The directors began their antics again, announcing the closing of the piece one minute and canceling the announcement the next, and making Carte's life generally miserable. Only after the entire cast and chorus had offered to take a cut of one third of their salaries was it decided to hang on awhile longer. Then, in August, Sullivan took over the conductorship of the "Classical Nights" at the prom concerts in Covent Garden and put on his programs a medley of airs from *Pinafore*. The very first night that he played it, it was encored three times. The public began to go to the Opéra Comique in increasing numbers, curious to see the operetta that had such a delightful score, and successfully launched *Pinafore* upon what was to be a run of two years.

Even so, Carte's troubles with his backers were not over. There was a clause in his lease requiring him, at some time to be determined to close the theater, for cleaning and alterations, and the directors conceived the brilliant idea of closing it for the Christmas season. During the Christmas season of 1877 *The Sorcerer* had done poor business; *ergo, Pinafore,* although by now it was selling out, would do the same. So close the theater they did, and kept the house dark until February, 1879. There could be no better evidence of *Pinafore*'s phenomenal drawing powers than the fact that this interruption failed to kill its run. Shortly after the reopening, Carte, disgusted, resolved to run The Comedy Opera Company singlehanded, and bought the directors out.

But there was more to come. Carte's lease (that is, his company's lease) on the theater was to expire on July thirty-first, and the ex-directors decided to claim the scenery and props as their property and to produce *Pinafore* elsewhere, without Carte. Accordingly, on the night of the thirtieth, two of them arrived at the theater with a fleet of moving vans and a crowd of knuckle men, prepared to carry off the production. A free-for-all started backstage that was clearly audible out front. Someone may or may not have shouted, "Fire!" At all events, the audience showed symptoms of what might easily have developed into a panic, until Grossmith came down to the footlights and explained the situation. The spectators, reassured, relaxed, the fight continued until the intruders had been thrown out, the show went on, and a pleasant time was had by all.

Nothing—or, practically nothing—daunted, the ex-directors threw together a *Pinafore* production of their own, and put it on, first at the Imperial Theatre, and later at the Olympic, just a door or so away from the Opéra Comique. For a time, the theatergoers crowded both theaters, apparently to make comparisons, while Gilbert and Sullivan issued a statement to the effect that the production at the Comique was the only authorized one. Then business at the Olympic fell off, the unauthorized company went to the provinces, and eventually collapsed.

What has always puzzled me is: *how* could the ex-directors stage a production that was not authorized by the authors? Surely a composer and librettist had some control over their own work, even in those free-and-easy days. Why didn't Gilbert and Sullivan simply bring suit for infringement of copyright? Whatever the reason, it seems to have been so obvious that no Gilbert and Sullivan biographer has ever taken the trouble to mention it. My own guess is that the two had signed a contract with the *company,* not Carte, and, when the split came, signed another contract with Carte, without being able to rescind the one with the directors. Even if unsound, it's a good theory, and I'm fond of it.

All during these final goings-on, Carte was not there. He had left for America early in July, to investigate reports of the spread of pirated performances of *Pinafore* overseas. There were plenty of them. In New York alone, eight companies were performing the piece, and the total number of performances throughout the country, on any given evening, must have approached a hundred. There were all sorts of variations and perversions of the original production. There was a children's *Pinafore* company (there was one in England, too. Lewis Carroll heard it, and beat his dear old breast into a pulp over hearing the tots sing, "He said 'Damme.' "); Philadelphia had an all-colored *Pinafore*; Boston an all-Catholic one. In the first New York production, a Miss Rose Temple played the role of Ralph Rackstraw, while in another, Little Buttercup was played by a man, who sang some interpolated sailor songs.

When Carte returned to London he reported all this. One fact that he had no need to report was the painful one that from all these performances neither he nor the authors were receiving a penny in royalties. This was owing to a copyright situation that will be explained later. The three held a council of war. If they couldn't collect on the current productions, there was at least one upon which they *could* collect. Accordingly, it was arranged that Gilbert, Sullivan, Alfred Cellier, and some picked members of the cast should go to New York and produce an authorized version of *Pinafore*.

The famous pair arrived in New York on November 5, 1879. *Pinafore* was now a year and a half old in America, and it might be expected that even an "authorized" version would have no further novelty for audiences that had been attending unauthorized ones for eighteen months. But, for one thing, Sullivan's orchestration was a revelation. The pirated versions had, of course, been made from the piano score—and anyone who has ever played one of those contemporaneous piano scores of Gilbert and Sullivan doesn't need to be told how little relation they bore to anything but the bare melodies and harmony. Incidentally, the preparations for the opening were attended by a phenomenon that is still a familiar one in the American theater. A few days before the opening the musicians went on strike. Sullivan and Cellier were preparing to go into the pit and accompany the singers on the piano and harmonium; but the grievance, whatever it was, was adjusted just in time.

They opened at the Fifth Avenue Theatre on the evening of December 1, 1879. Here is part of a contemporary report of the performance:

"Last evening, *H.M.S. Pinafore* was in command of its builders. Mr. Sullivan conducted in the orchestra, and the master hand was clearly discernible in the result. It seemed already as though human ingenuity had been exhausted to provide appropriate business for the opera, and that everything thinkable had been thought of. But last night's performance was everywhere studded with new points. When the scene opened, the sailors were all seen at work, flemishing down the ropes and attending to various ship's duties, while the whole was under the supervision of the busy and important little Midshipman. This gave an animation to the first scene that it generally lacks. . . . But the really noticeable difference in the interpretation was the orchestration. There was breadth, color, and tone, together with a harmonious blending with the vocalism which was utterly wanting in what may be called the home-made *Pinafores*."

Sullivan was not the only author who was visible. If the reviewer had noticed, he might have seen Gilbert likewise, in uniform, as one of the chorus, so placed that he could keep an eye on the performance. The reception was, of course, riotous; and when the authors appeared before the curtain at the end, Gilbert made a short speech of thanks. This was not, he said, a new work; in fact, he had been led to believe that it had been performed in New York before. "It has been our purpose," he explained, "to produce something that should be innocent but not imbecile."

The authorized *Pinafore* got off to a fine start; but it was not the chief preoccupation of Gilbert and Sullivan. They were embarked on quite another project. But of that, more anon. Let us hear *Pinafore* first.

THE STORY

ACT I

On the deck of H.M.S. *Pinafore*, the gallant crew, being rather pleased with itself, expresses this professional pride in the stirring strains of WE SAIL THE OCEAN BLUE. They are engaged in their honest toil when of a sudden Little Buttercup, the rosiest, the roundest, and the reddest of bumboat-women, comes aboard to sell them ribbons and laces for their sweethearts. She points out that although I'M CALLED LITTLE BUTTERCUP, and in spite of her jolly appearance, a mysterious secret weighs heavy on her heart. Ralph Rackstraw, who, though a simple sailor, lowly born, is yet the smartest lad in all the fleet, comes up the hatchway and confides to the entire crew that he is in love with A MAIDEN FAIR TO SEE—who is, unfortunately, the Captain's daughter. A villainous sailor, Dick Deadeye, dares to say that captains' daughters are not in the habit of marrying humble seamen. He is roundly scolded by the sailors for this heresy, and saved from physical harm only by the entrance of an officer who makes it clear that I AM THE CAPTAIN OF THE PINAFORE.

Left alone with Little Buttercup, the Captain admits that he is worried because his daughter, Josephine, refuses to marry Sir Joseph Porter, K.C.B., First Lord of the Admiralty. Buttercup leaves and Josephine enters, murmuring sadly, SORRY HER LOT who loves too well. She tells her father that, while she esteems Sir Joseph, she loves a humble sailor aboard the *Pinafore*. But after hearing her father's kindly (but class-conscious) arguments, she agrees to think no more of one so far beneath her and to listen to the declarations of Sir Joseph, who is at this moment approaching on his barge, accompanied as always by his retinue of admiring sisters and cousins and aunts, led by Cousin Hebe.

The sailors huzzah, and the female relations twitter, while Sir Joseph, a dapper though elderly gentleman, announces that I AM THE MONARCH OF THE SEA and proceeds to tell how he attained this high station, outlining what happened WHEN I WAS A LAD. He admonishes the Captain never to look down upon sailors, since they are as good as anyone else, except, of course, Sir Joseph himself.

When the Captain and his exalted guest go below, Ralph Rackstraw confesses his love to Josephine. Although she returns this happy passion, she pretends pride (not sartorial interest) when ordering him to REFRAIN, AUDACIOUS TAR, your suit from pressing. But then Ralph takes matters (and also a pistol) into his own hands and threatens to shoot himself. Naturally, this makes Josephine confess her love and they plan to elope—which delights all the sailors, except Dick Deadeye.

ACT II

Night has fallen, and the Captain paces the deck, audibly brooding over his sorrows (and also giving a pretty good synopsis of Act I as he does so). Little Buttercup comes and gazes at him sentimentally. It develops that the Captain secretly loves Little Buttercup, but, as he tells her, because of their difference in social standing, they can never be more than friends. Little Buttercup warns him not to be too sure, since THINGS ARE SELDOM WHAT THEY SEEM. Enter Sir Joseph with Josephine, to whom he offers his heart and exalted rank. Under the impression that her unresponsiveness is caused by his high station, Sir Joseph suggests she should NEVER MIND THE WHY AND WHEREFORE. This plea is only too effective, since Sir Joseph's democratic sentiments strengthen Josephine's determination to elope with Ralph Rackstraw.

But that villainous betrayer, Dick Deadeye, furtively whispering KIND CAPTAIN, I'VE IMPORTANT INFORMATION, tells his master about the merry maiden and the tar. His paternal and social instincts outraged, the Captain hides as the elopement party comes in, CAREFULLY ON TIPTOE STEALING. At the crucial moment he leaps forward and forbids them to proceed. Then Sir Joseph's romantic female relations and the equally romantic sailors tell the Captain not to scorn Ralph Rackstraw—HE IS AN ENGLISHMAN.

To everyone's horror, including his own, the Captain is so furious that he allows himself to say "Damme!" Sir Joseph immediately comes aboard and berates him for swearing at a British sailor. Nevertheless, Sir Joseph's own fury on learning of the elopement is awful to behold. He inquires as to whether there is such a thing as a dungeon on board and, on finding that there is, orders Ralph to be dragged off to it in chains. The lovers make ready to part in the tearful strains of FAREWELL, MY OWN.

But wait! In the nick of time Little Buttercup steps forward. She explains that when she was young and charming she practiced baby farming. She further adds that when the infant Ralph Rackstraw and the infant Captain were entrusted to her care, she mixed those children up. The nub of the matter is, she concludes, that Ralph is really the Captain and the Captain is really Ralph.

Naturally, this solves everything. Sir Joseph can no longer think of marrying Josephine, the daughter of a humble A.B., so he contents himself with his devoted Cousin Hebe. Ralph and Josephine can at last be married, and the Captain, overjoyed at now being a mere member of the crew, can marry Little Buttercup. So everyone is happy—with the possible exception of the audience, who have always wanted more.

We Sail the Ocean Blue

With vigor and ponderously CHORUS of MEN

We_ sail the o-cean blue, And our sau-cy ship's a beau-ty; We're_ so-ber men and true, And at-ten-tive to our du-ty. When the balls whis-tle free o'er the bright_ blue sea, We stand_ to our guns all_ day._ When at

ten - tive to our du - ty; Our sau - cy ship's a beau - ty, We're at -

ten - tive to our du - ty; We're so - ber men and true, We sail the

o - - - - cean blue!

I'm Called Little Buttercup

Moderate Waltz tempo

LITTLE BUTTERCUP

I'm called lit - tle But-ter-cup, Dear lit - tle

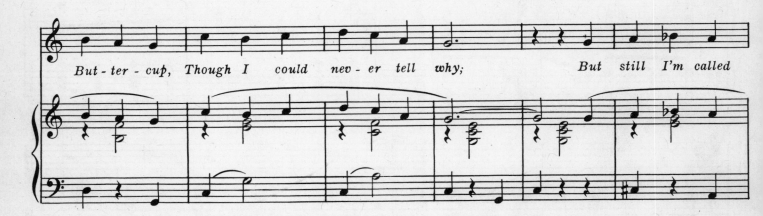

But-ter-cup, Though I could nev-er tell why; But still I'm called

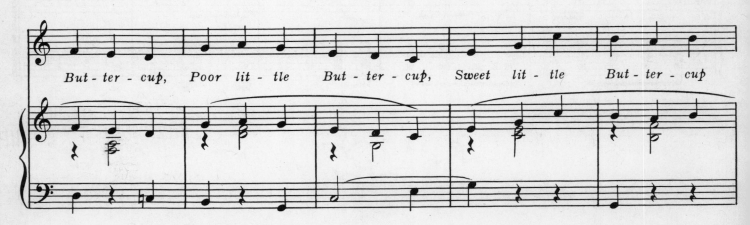

But-ter-cup, Poor lit - tle But-ter-cup, Sweet lit - tle But-ter-cup

I. I've snuff and to-bac-cy, and ex-cel-lent jack-y; I've scis-sors and watch-es and knives; I've rib-bons and lac-es to set off the fac-es Of pret-ty young sweet-hearts and wives. I've trea-cle and tof-fee, I've tea and I've cof-fee, Soft tom-my and suc-cu-lent chops; I've chick-ens and co-nies, And

pret - ty po - lo - nies, And ex - cel - lent pep - per-mint drops. Then

buy of your But - ter - cup, Dear lit - tle But - ter - cup; Sail - ors should

nev - er be shy; So buy of your But - ter - cup,

Poor lit - tle But - ter - cup; Come, of your But - ter - cup buy.

A Maiden Fair to See

With restraint, as a ballad

RALPH

A maid-en fair to see, The pearl of min-strel-sy, A bud of blush-ing beau-ty; For whom proud no-bles sigh, And with each oth-er vie To do her me-nial's du-ty. To do her me-nial's

CHORUS

RALPH

du - ty. A suit - or, low - ly born, With hope - less pas - sion torn, And

poor be - yond de - ny - ing, Has dared for her to pine, At

CHORUS

whose ex - alt - ed shrine A world of wealth is sigh - ing. A world of wealth is

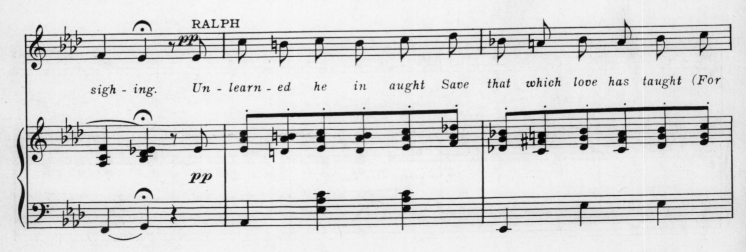

RALPH

sigh - ing. Un - learn - ed he in aught Save that which love has taught (For

love had been his tu - tor); Oh, pit - y, pit - y me, Our

cap - tain's daugh - ter, she, And I that low - ly suit - or. Oh,

pit - y, pit - y me, Our cap-tain's daugh - ter, she, And I that low - ly

suit - or.

I Am the Captain of the Pinafore

Sprightly

CAPTAIN CORCORAN

1. I am the Cap-tain of the
(2. I) do my best to sat-is-

MEN   CAPTAIN CORCORAN

Pin-a-fore! And a right-good cap-tain, too! You're ver-y, ver-y good, And,
fy you all! And with you we're quite con-tent. You're ex-ceed-ing-ly po-lite, And I

MEN

be it un-der-stood, I com-mand a right good crew. We're
think it on-ly right To re-turn the com-pli-ment. We're ex-

ver - y, ver - y good, And,   be it un-der-stood, He com-mands a___ right good
ceed-ing-ly po - lite, And he   thinks it on-ly right To re - turn the__ com-pli-

CAPTAIN

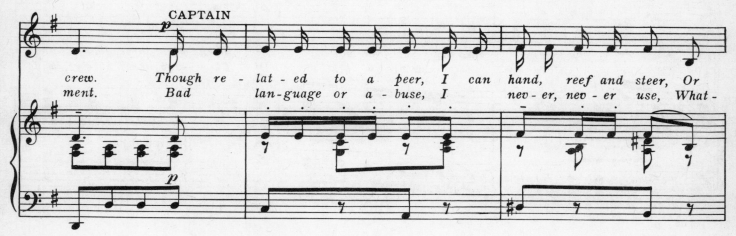

crew.   Though re - lat - ed   to a peer, I can hand, reef and steer, Or
ment.   Bad   lan-guage or a - buse, I   nev - er, nev - er use, What-

ship   a sel - va - gee;   I am nev - er known to quail At the
ev - er the e - mer - gen - cy;   Though "both - er it" I may Oc -

MEN

fu - ry of a gale, And I'm   nev - er, nev - er sick at sea!   What,
ca - sion-al - ly say,   I   nev - er use a big, big D!   What,

CAPTAIN · MEN · CAPTAIN

nev - er? No, nev - er! What nev - er?— Hard-ly
nev - er? No, nev - er! What nev - er?— Hard-ly

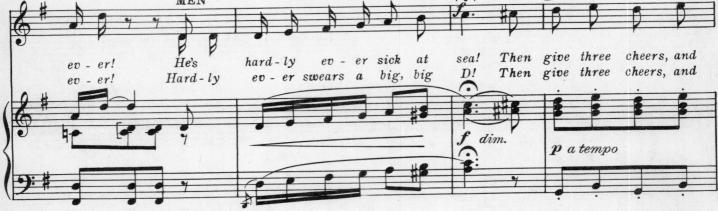

MEN

ev - er! He's hard-ly ev - er sick at sea! Then give three cheers, and
ev - er! Hard-ly ev - er swears a big, big D! Then give three cheers, and

one cheer more, For the har - dy Cap-tain of the Pin - a - fore! Then give three cheers, and
one cheer more, For the well-bred Cap-tain of the Pin - a - fore! Then give three cheers, and

one cheer more, For the Cap-tain of the Pin - a - fore! 2. I
one cheer more, For the Cap-tain of the Pin - a - -fore!—

Sorry Her Lot

Slowly, with expression

mf — *p*

JOSEPHINE

mp

1. Sor-ry her lot____ who loves_ too well, Heav-y the
2. Sad is the hour____ when sets_ the sun, Dark is the

heart____ that hopes but vain - ly, Sad____ are the sighs_ that
night____ to earth's poor daugh - ters, When____ to the ark_ the

own the spell Ut-tered by eyes____ that speak too plain - ly; Sor-ry her lot____ who
wea-ried one Flies from the emp - ty waste of wa - ters. Sad is the hour__ when

I Am the Monarch of the Sea

Very lively

SIR JOSEPH

I am the mon-arch of the sea, The rul-er of the Queen's Na - vee, Whose praise Great Brit - ain loud - ly chants.

COUSIN HEBE

And we are his sis-ters and his cous-ins and his aunts, And

COUSIN HEBE and CHORUS

we are his sis-ters and his cous-ins and his aunts, His sis-ters and his cous-ins and his

When I Was a Lad

Brightly, but not too fast

SIR JOSEPH

1. When I was a lad I served a term As
(2. As) of - fice boy I made such a mark That they
(3. In) serv - ing writs I made such a name That an

of - fice boy to an at - tor - ney's firm. I cleaned the win - dows and I
gave me the post_ of a jun - ior clerk. I served the writs with a
ar - ti - cled clerk_ I___ soon be - came; I wore clean col - lars and a

staccato

[66]

swept the floor, And I pol-ished up the han-dle of the big front door. He
smile so bland, And I cop-ied all the let-ters in a big round hand. He
brand-new suit For the pass ex - am - i - na-tion at the In - sti - tute. For the

pol-ished up the han-dle of the big front door. I pol-ished up that han-dle so
cop-ied all the let-ters in a big round hand. I cop-ied all the let-ters in a
pass ex - am - i - na-tion at the In - sti - tute. That pass ex - am - i - na-tion did so

SIR JOSEPH

care - ful - lee That now I am the rul - er of the Queen's Na - vee! He
hand so free That now I am the rul - er of the Queen's Na - vee! He
well for me That now I am the rul - er of the Queen's Na - vee! That

CHORUS

pol - ished up that han-dle so care - ful - lee That now he is the rul - er of the
cop - ied all the let-ters in a hand so free That now he is the rul - er of the
pass ex - am - i - na-tion did so well for him That now he is the rul - er of the

[67]

Refrain, Audacious Tar

Fast and passionately

Josephine 1.Re -
Ralph. 2.Proud

frain, au - da -cious tar, Your suit from press - ing, Re - mem - ber what you
la - dy, have your way, Un - feel - ing beau - ty! You speak, and I o-

are, And whom ad - dress - ing, Re - frain, au - da - cious tar, Your
bey, It is— my— du - ty! I am the low - liest tar That

suit from press - ing, Re - mem - ber what you are, And whom ad - dress - ing, Re-
sails the wa - ter, And you, proud maid - en, are My cap - tain's daugh - ter. Proud

frain, au-da-cious tar, Re - mem - ber what you are. (Aside) I'd
la - dy, have your way, You speak, and I o - bey. (Aside) My

Slower

laugh my rank to scorn In un - ion____ ho - ly, Were
heart, with an - guish torn, Bows down____ be - - fore her. She

he more high - ly born Or I____ more____ low - ly. I'd
laughs my love to scorn, Yet I____ a - dore her. My

laugh my rank to scorn In un - ion ho - ly, Were he more high - ly
heart, with an - guish torn, Bows down be - fore her. She laughs my love to

follow the voice

1.
born Or I more low - ly.
scorn, Yet I a -

2. In tempo again   JOSEPHINE
- dore her. Re - frain, au-da-cious

tar, Your suit from press - ing! Proud la - dy, have your way, Un-feel-ing

beau - ty!
Josephine (lower note)   I'd laugh my rank to scorn, In un - ion
Ralph (upper note)   My heart, with an - guish torn, Bows down be -

ho - ly, Were he more high - ly born___ Or I
fore her. She laughs my love to scorn,___ Yet I

more low - ly.
a - dore___ her.

Things Are Seldom What They Seem

Moderately fast

Little Buttercup 1.Things are sel-dom what they seem,
Captain Corcoran 2.Tho' I'm an - y - thing but clev-er,

Skim milk mas - quer - ades as cream; High -lows pass as pat - ent leath-ers;
I could talk like that for - ev - er: Once a cat was killed by care;

Jack-daws strut in pea-cock's feath-ers. Capt. Corcoran Ver - y true, so they do.
On - ly brave de - serve the fair. Little Buttercup Ver - y true, so they do.

Little Buttercup Black sheep dwell in ev -'ry fold; All that glit - ters is not gold;
Captain Corcoran Wink is oft - en good as nod; Spoils the child who spares the rod;

Storks turn out to be but logs; Bulls are but in-flat-ed frogs. Capt. C. So they be,
Thirst-y lambs run fox-y dan-gers; Dogs are found in man-y man-gers. Buttercup Fre-quent-lee,

fre-quent-lee. Buttercup Drops the wind and stops the mill; Tur-bot is am-
I a-gree. Capt. Cor. Paw of cat the chest-nut snatch-es; Worn-out gar-ments

bi-tious brill; Gild the farth-ing if you will, Yet it is a farth-ing still.
show new patch-es; On-ly count the chick that hatch-es; Men are grown-up catch-y-catch-ies.

Capt.C. Yes, I know, That is so. Tho' to catch your drift I'm striv-ing, It is shad-y, it is
Buttercup Yes, I know, That is so. Tho' to catch my drift he's striv-ing, I'll dis-sem-ble, I'll dis-

shad-y; I don't see at what you're driv-ing, Mys-tic la-dy, mys-tic la-dy.
sem-ble! When he sees at what I'm driv-ing, Let him trem-ble, let him trem-ble!

Never Mind the Why and Wherefore

Joyful and full of life

Captain Corcoran 1. Nev-er mind the why and
Sir Joseph 2. Nev-er mind the why and
Josephine 3. Nev-er mind the why and

where-fore, Love can lev-el ranks, and there-fore, Though his Lord-ship's sta-tion's
where-fore, Love can lev-el ranks, and there-fore, Though your nau-ti-cal re-
where-fore, Love can lev-el ranks, and there-fore, I ad-mit the ju-ris-

might-y, Though stu-pen-dous be his brain, Though her tastes are mean and
la-tion In my set could scarce-ly pass, Though you oc-cu-py a
dic-tion; A-bly have you play'd your part, You have car-ried firm con-

_f_ ALL THREE

Rend with songs the air a-bove, For the man who owns her love,

Rend with songs the air— a - bove, For the man who owns her

love. —

f a tempo

Kind Captain, I've Important Information

Moderately lively

Dick Deadeye 1. Kind
(Capt. Corcoran 2. Good)
(Dick Deadeye 3. Kind)
(Capt. Corcoran 4. Good)

Cap - tain, I've im - por - tant in - for - ma - tion, Sing
fel - low, in co - nun - drums you are speak - ing, Sing
Cap - tain, your young la - dy is a - sigh - ing, Sing
fel - low, you have giv - en time - ly warn - ing, Sing

hey, the kind com - man - der that you are, A -
hey, the mys - tic sail - or that you are; The
hey, the sim - ple Cap - tain that you are, This
hey, the thought - ful sail - or that you are; I'll

bout a cer - tain in - ti - mate re - la - tion, Sing
an - swer to them vain - ly I am seek - ing, Sing
ver - y night with Rack - straw to be fly - ing, Sing
talk to Mas - ter Rack - straw in the morn - ing, Sing

Carefully on Tiptoe Stealing

Moderately

MEN

1. Care-ful - ly on tip - toe steal - ing, Breath-ing gent - ly as we may, Ev - 'ry
2. (Pull a-) shore in fash - ion stead - y, Hy - men will de - fray the fare, For a

step with cau - tion feel - ing, We __ will __ soft - ly steal a -
cler - gy - man is read - y To __ u - nite the hap - py

way. Good - ness me! Why, what was that? Si - lent
pair. Good - ness me! Why, what was that? Si - lent

DEADEYE

He Is an Englishman

Farewell, My Own

With warmth and animation — RALPH

Fare - well, my

own, Light of my life, fare - well! For crime un -

known I go to a dun - geon cell. — JOSEPHINE — I will a -

tone; In the mean - time, fare - well! And all a -

lone Re-joice in your dun-geon cell! ____ A bone, ____ a

SIR JOSEPH

bone, ____ I'll pick with this sail-or fell; Let him be

shown At once to his dun-geon cell. He'll hear no

ENSEMBLE

tone ___ Of the maid-en he loves so well! No tel-e-

phone Com-mu-ni-cates with his cell! But when is known The

LITTLE BUTTERCUP

se - cret I have to tell, Wide will be thrown The door of his dun - geon cell.

f *mf* ENSEMBLE

Fare - well, my own, Light of my life, fare - well!

cresc. molto *ff*

And all a - lone Re - joice in your dun - geon, your dun -

rit *molto rit*

geon cell!

solemnly

THE PIRATES OF PENZANCE

OR

The Slave of Duty

THE PIRATES OF PENZANCE

OR
The Slave of Duty

WHILE the ostensible reason for Gilbert and Sullivan's trip to America was to stage the authorized version of *Pinafore*, it was not the principal one. Here is Sir Arthur Sullivan's own account of why they went:

"Of course Gilbert and myself had been kept informed of the unique business which *Pinafore* was doing in America, and our visit was prompted by the notion that, as authors of the piece, we ought to profit by it. Meanwhile, we did not trust to the *Pinafore* opera to do us any material monetary good in America; we determined to produce our next opera in the States first and in Great Britain afterwards. The Americans acknowledged that the author had a right in his unpublished work in the same way that he could lay claim to his own personal apparel or any other form of property, and only lost his prerogative after it had been published. So all we could do was to follow the course I have indicated, and produce our piece in America first, and get our own company well under way before others could bring out their imitations."

Between the United States and Russia today there is no reciprocal copyright arrangement. Any American can take any piece of music published in Russia and print it or perform it without paying a cent of royalty and without danger of successful prosecution for violation of copyright (the converse is equally true in Russia, of course). If, on the other hand, a Russian should bring to this country a piece of *manuscript* music, and an American should get hold of it and print it or exploit it, then the Russian could prosecute him for stealing his personal property.

Such was precisely the condition of affairs existing between Great Britain and the United States in the days of Gilbert and Sullivan. Their only means of protecting their performing and publishing rights in an operetta was to keep the libretto and score in manuscript and produce it here themselves. This, as Sullivan points

out, they had decided to do. When they arrived in New York, they brought a new operetta with them—or, at any rate, most of it. Gilbert had finished the libretto in England, and Sullivan had composed most of the music for the second act. His music for the first act, however, existed only in the form of sketches. These he had, unbelievably, forgotten to bring with him, so that he had to rewrite Act I from memory.

There were rumors that the famous pair were at work on a new piece, and Gilbert, upon being questioned by the press, didn't deny them. The general impression was that it would be called *The Robbers* and that it contained one situation wherein six burglars make love to the six daughters of the man whose house they are robbing. As you can see, by reading the plot synopsis, there was a grain of truth in the assumption.

The authorized *Pinafore* did enormous business at first; but, after all, Americans had been seeing *Pinafore* productions for eighteen months. From terrific, business fell off to excellent, then to pretty good. Obviously the production would not run indefinitely, and if the authors were not to be faced with a darkened theater the new piece must be ready before the new year.

Gilbert's work having already been completed, this meant work, hard work, for Sullivan. The job would have looked formidable enough under any conditions; as things were, with Sullivan conducting *Pinafore* every night (Cellier had to rehearse what there was ready of the new piece), attending public dinners, and receiving dinners, it looked impossible. To make matters worse, he was suffering agonies from recurrent attacks of his old kidney complaint. Somehow, however, between the beginning and the end of December, 1879, he managed to compose the first act and orchestrate the entire score.

There is a sidelight on the orchestration that seems to explain how he was able to accomplish the seeming impossible. One day, thirty-odd years ago, I was discussing Sullivan's first visit to America with my old music teacher, Oscar Coon (he was then about seventy-five years old), when he remarked, casually, "You know, I scored several numbers in that show for Sullivan."

I pricked up my ears. Here was news! Naturally, I wanted details, and he explained. Sullivan was living in a hotel on East Twentieth Street, composing and scoring at the same time. He would send for Coon, and hand him the sketch for a number, together with an incomplete score, some of it written out in full, some of it with the instrumentation merely indicated. Coon would then fill in the orchestration, in accordance with Sullivan's directions. The old man may have been embroidering, of course. If he was, it was the first lie I ever heard him tell. As a matter of fact, there would have been nothing perfunctory or unethical in Sullivan's doing such a thing. In light opera, which consists largely of melody and simple accompaniment, there inevitably occur passages, of from eight to sixteen or even thirty-two measures in length, where the instrumentation, once set, naturally continues unchanged for some time. The composer usually fills in such passages himself. On the other hand, he can save himself a lot of manual labor by leaving them to be filled in by almost any competent arranger. The result, in sound, will be the same.

However he may have done it, he finished just in time. After the dress rehearsal, on the night of December thirtieth, he went home and started the overture, finishing it at five in the morning and rehearsing it at eleven. At eight, on the evening of December 31, 1879, he was back in the pit of the Fifth Avenue Theatre to conduct the first performance anywhere of *The Pirates of Penzance; or, Love and Duty.* The cast was as follows:

Major-General Stanley J. H. Ryley	*Sergeant of Police* F. Clifton
	Mabel Blanche Roosevelt*
The Pirate King Mr. Broccolini	*Edith* Jessie Bond*
	Kate Rosina Brandram*
Samuel Furneaux Cook	*Isabel* Billie Barlow
Frederic Hugh Talbot*	*Ruth* Alice Barnett

The night before, at the Bijou Theatre in Paignton, England, a first British performance of *The Pirates* had taken place. This was a scratch affair, produced by a traveling *Pinafore* company, put on "for one time only" before an audience of about fifty, solely to protect the British performing rights. One historical feature of the performance, which went unnoticed at the time, was

_____
*Imported from England.

that Richard Mansfield, destined later to be one of America's great dramatic stars, played the role of Major General Stanley.

Sullivan's poor health was not the only handicap under which the New York opening labored. Soon after the orchestra rehearsals had begun, the musicians again went on strike, claiming that the score came under the head of grand opera rather than operetta and that they should, accordingly, be paid more. The manager of the Fifth Avenue Theatre sought to settle the dispute by the happy device of reminding the players that they were playing the music of England's greatest living composer. So they used that fact, too, as an argument for getting higher pay.

Sullivan then stepped in. First declaring his pleasure at being afforded the privilege of conducting such a brilliant orchestra, he regretfully announced that the orchestra of Covent Garden, in London, while not so brilliant, perhaps, did happen to be at liberty for the time being and was prepared to sail for America as soon as he should cable. The musicians finally decided that the new piece was operetta, after all.

The opening night in New York was a triumph. No such music had ever been heard before in a light opera, and even the authorized *Pinafore* production had not prepared the spectators for the elaborate settings and perfect direction that the new work presented. There could be no possible doubt of its success.

But *The Pirates of Penzance* (by the way, do you realize that, to a British audience, that title sounds as *The Pirates of Atlantic City* would to an American one?) had not conquered the Pirates of New York. Remember that the producer of a pirated version of words or music was criminally liable *only* if he took possession of the actual manuscript. So long as he gave the authors credit, he was safe from prosecution, particularly as one American court had ruled that a public performance was tantamount to publication and therefore made the work public property. The theater began to be haunted by musical spies, copyists and transcribers who had been hired to take down the airs as they were sung or played. Not only did certain freebooters produce abbreviated and distorted versions of the piece, but publishers issued albums, described as "Recollections" or "Impressions" of *The Pirates of Penzance*. Every night, after the performance, the score and parts were locked up in a safe. Even so, someone offered the concertmaster of the orchestra a hundred dollars for a copy of the first-violin part.

Gilbert and Sullivan accordingly decided that the best thing to do was to skim the cream of the American market while the skimming was good. They rehearsed three or four road companies and sent them out on tours that, as a whole, returned them a highly substantial profit. During this part of their stay Sullivan went up to Boston, where he conducted his cantata, *The Prodigal Son*, with the Handel and Haydn Society. The last of the road companies started from Buffalo, and the author-producers profited by the occasion to visit Niagara Falls; after which, Sullivan went for a brief visit to Canada, and Gilbert returned to New York to wind up some business affairs. The pair sailed for England on March 3, 1880.

Arriving in London, they immediately started rehearsals for the British production, *Pinafore* just having closed after a record-smashing run of something over 675 performances. In as much as there was no longer any point to keeping the music in manuscript, Sullivan gave the vocal score to his publishers. In less than three weeks all was in readiness, and on the evening of April 3, 1880, *The Pirates of Penzance; or, The Slave of Duty* (notice the changed subtitle) opened at the Opéra Comique. Grossmith was General Stanley, Barrington was the Sergeant, and Richard Temple was the Pirate King. The day after the opening, Sullivan wrote to his mother that the libretto, "wonderfully funny in parts, is beautifully written for music, as is all Gilbert does. The music is infinitely superior in every way to the *Pinafore*—'tunier' and more developed, of a higher class altogether. I think that in time it will be more popular."

Sullivan was not a good guesser as regards the ultimate fate of the *Pirates* score; but at the moment one thing was certain: Gilbert and Sullivan had another hit on their hands.

THE STORY

ACT I

On the rocky coast of Cornwall, a band of pirates are employed in toasting the newly won piratehood of their apprentice, Frederic, who today is freed from his indentures. Frederic alone is despondent, and Ruth, the piratical maid of all work, explains why. It seems that WHEN FREDERIC WAS A LITTLE LAD she was his stupid nursery maid, on breakers always steering, and she did not catch a word aright through being hard of hearing. She apprenticed Frederic to a pirate instead of to a *pilot*, as his father had requested.

Frederic is thoroughly cast down, since he feels that he must go back to the world of honest men and that it is his duty to devote himself heart and soul to the extermination of his beloved pirates. He pleads with them to forswear their evil trade, but to the Pirate King it is OH BETTER FAR TO LIVE AND DIE under the brave black flag they fly than play a sanctimonious part with a pirate head and a pirate heart.

Ruth begs Frederic to take her with him, but although he believes her to be beautiful, having never seen another woman, he declines, mentioning that a lady of forty-seven might possibly be too old a wife for a lad of twenty-one. Unfortunately for Ruth, Frederic just then sees true beauty for the first time as a bevy of maidens trips lightly in, picnic-bound, CLIMBING OVER ROCKY MOUNTAIN.

They are shocked by his pirate attire and he pleads in vain, OH, IS THERE NOT ONE MAIDEN BREAST that will be moved by such an one as he? There doesn't appear to be one, no, no—not one.

Yes, one! Mabel! Entering, she courageously volunteers to sacrifice her future to save Frederic's piece of mind, berates her sisters, and bids Frederic, POOR WANDERING ONE, to take heart—her heart, in fact.

The pirates enter stealthily. Each seizes a girl, all having been struck with the happy thought that here is a first-rate opportunity to get married with impunity.

This fell plan falls foul of the fact, which Mabel announces, that all the girls are wards in chancery, their father being a major-general. This is substantiated by the arrival of Mabel's father, who drives the point home by making it quite clear that I am the very MODEL OF A MODERN MAJOR-GENERAL.

While this impresses the pirates, they persist in demanding General Stanley's daughters in marriage. But he plays upon their softheartedness by announcing that he is an orphan (the news has got about that the Pirates of Penzance, being orphans themselves, are very tenderhearted about all others). They allow him to go in peace with his daughters and with Frederic, while poor Ruth remains reluctantly behind.

ACT II

In a ruined chapel, before the tombs of his ancestors (he is their descendant by purchase, since he has bought the estate just recently), General Stanley shamefacedly confesses to Frederic and Mabel that he is not really an orphan. Frederic comforts him, tells him of his preparations for the coming pirate purge, and is proposing to Mabel when the policemen, who are to exterminate the pirates, enter and put off their expedition somewhat by explaining how uncomfortable they feel WHEN THE FOEMAN BARES HIS STEEL. Frederic is about to join them in their glorious exploit when Ruth and the Pirate King arrive, announcing that they have just discovered a most ingenious paradox. Frederic was born on leap-year day and thus won't reach his twenty-first birthday until 1940. He is, therefore, still legally apprenticed to the pirates.

Being a slave of duty, Frederic again resumes his indentures and is forced in all honor to tell the pirates that General Stanley is not really an orphan. AH, LEAVE ME NOT TO PINE, Mabel begs him, but Frederic's sense of duty wins out.

The police return and, explaining that A POLICEMAN'S LOT IS NOT A HAPPY ONE, reluctantly plan to arrest the pirates. Hearing a pirate chorus in the distance, they conceal themselves. The pirates enter, stealing WITH CATLIKE TREAD upon their prey, General Stanley. Just as the pirates are about to do away with the Major-General, the constabulary springs into action—and is rapidly overwhelmed. All are about to be dispatched when they play their trump card, drawing small Union Jacks from their bosoms and charging the pirates to yield, in Queen Victoria's name. Naturally, the pirates yield immediately, because, with all their faults, they love their Queen. Ruth secures their pardon by revealing that they are not common criminals at all, but are noblemen who have gone wrong. So of course they are forgiven, and General Stanley invites them all to resume their ranks and legislative duties and to marry his daughters.

When Frederic Was a Little Lad

With speed, but ponderously

RUTH

1. When
2. I
3. I

Fred-'ric was a— lit-tle lad He— proved so brave and dar-ing, His
was a stu-pid— nur'-s'ry maid, On— break-ers al-ways steer-ing, And I
soon found out, be- yond all doubt, The— scope of this dis- as-ter, But I

fa- ther thought he'd— 'pren-tice him To— some ca-reer sea-far-ing. I—
did not catch the— word a- right, Through be-ing hard of hear-ing; Mis-
had- n't the face to re-turn to my place, And— break it to my mas-ter. A—

was, a- las! his— nur-s'ry maid, And— so it fell to my lot To
tak- ing my in- struc-tions,which With- in my brain did gy-rate, I
nur- s'ry maid is— not a- fraid Of— what you peo- ple call work, So I

take and bind the_ prom-is-ing boy Ap - pren-tice to a pi-lot! A
took and bound this_ prom-is-ing boy Ap - pren-tice to a pi-rate! A
made up my mind to_ go as a kind Of pi-rat-i-cal maid-of- all-work. And

life not bad for a har-dy lad, Though_ sure-ly not a
sad mis-take it ____ was to make, And_ doom him to a
that is how you__ find me now, A ___ mem-ber of your

high lot, Though I'm a nurse, you might do worse Than make your boy a
vile lot. I bound him to a pi-rate, you! In-stead of to a
shy lot, Which you would-n't have found, had he been bound Ap - pren-tice to a

pi-lot!
pi-lot!
pi-lot!

Oh Better Far to Live and Die

Moderately fast

f *marcato*

mp **PIRATE KING**

1. Oh bet - ter far to live_ and die
2. When I sal - ly forth to seek_ my prey I

Un - der the brave black flag I fly, Than play a sanc - ti - mo - nious part, With a
help my - self in a roy - al way; I sink a few more ships, it's true, Than a

Climbing Over Rocky Mountain

Gracefully and not too fast

CHORUS of GIRLS

Climb-ing o-ver_ rock-y moun-tain, Skip-ping riv-u - let and foun-tain,

Pass-ing where the_ wil - lows_ quiv - er,

bright sea - shore they gain; Scal-ing rough and__ rug-ged pass-es,

Climb the har-dy__ lit-tle lass-es Till__ the __ bright sea -

shore they gain!

Oh, Is There Not One Maiden Breast

Slowly and tenderly

FREDERIC

Oh, is there not one maid-en breast Which does not feel the mor-al beau-ty Of mak-ing world-ly in-ter-est Sub-or-di-nate to sense of

FREDERIC

in-ter-est Sub - or - di - nate to sense of du - ty!

Oh, is there not one maid-en here Whose home-ly face and bad com - plex - ion Have caused all hope to dis-ap-pear Of ev - er win-ning man's af - fec - tion? To such an one, if such there be, I swear by Heav-en's arch a - bove you, If you will cast your eyes on me, How-

Poor Wandering One

p MABEL

an - y heart_ but ours! Take heart, fair days will

shine;_ Take an - y heart, take mine! Ah! _____ Ah! _____

poco a

Ah! Ah!

poco cresc. *f*

p a tempo

Poor wan - d'ring one! _____ Tho' thou hast sure - ly strayed,_

p a tempo

cresc. e più espr.

Take heart of grace, Thy steps re - trace, Poor_ wan- d'ring

cresc. e più espr.

one!   *Ah, ah!* — *Ah, ah,*   *ah!*   *Ah, ah!*

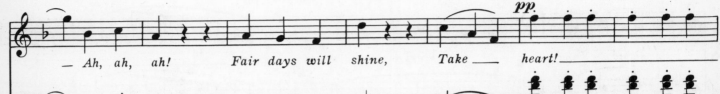

— *Ah, ah,*   *ah!*   *Fair days will*   *shine,*   *Take* —— *heart!*

Take —— *mine!*   *Take* —

heart!

Model of a Modern Major-General

Cheerfully

ff

MAJOR-GENERAL

p

pp *p*

1. I   am the ver-y mod-el of a   mod-ern Ma-jor-Gin-er-al; I've
2. I   know our myth-ic his-to-ry, King   Ar-thur's and Sir Car-a-doc's; I

in-for-ma-tion veg-e-ta-ble,   an-i-mal and min-er-al;   I
an-swer hard a-cros-tics, I've a   pret-ty taste for par-a-dox;   I

know the Kings of Eng - land, and I quote the fights his - tor - i - cal, From
quote in el - e - gi - acs all the crimes of He - lio - ga - ba - lus! In

Mar - a - thon to Wa - ter - loo, in or - der cat - e - gor - i - cal; I'm
con - ics I can floor pe - cu - li - ar - i - ties pa - rab - o - lus. I can

ver - y well ac - quain - ted, too, with mat - ters math - e - mat - i - cal, I
tell un - doubt - ed Ra - pha - els from Ge - rard Dows and Zoff - an - ies. I

un - der - stand e - qua - tions, both the sim - ple and quad - rat - i - cal, A -
know the croak - ing cho - rus from the "Frogs" of Ar - is - toph - a - nes! Then

bout bi - no - mial the - o - rem I'm teem - ing with a lot of news,
I can hum a fugue of which I've heard the mu - sic's din a - fore,

With man-y cheer-ful facts a-bout the square of the hy-pot-e-nuse.
And whis-tle all the airs from that in-fer-nal non-sense, Pin-a-fore!

CHORUS

With man-y cheer-ful facts a-bout the square of the hy-pot-e-nuse, With
And whis-tle all the airs from that in-fer-nal non-sense, Pin-a-fore, And

man-y cheer-ful facts a-bout the square of the hy-pot-e-nuse, With
whis-tle all the airs from that in-fer-nal non-sense, Pin-a-fore, And

man-y cheer-ful facts a-bout the square of the hy-pot-e-pot-e-
whis-tle all the airs from that in-fer-nal non-sense, Pin-a-pin-a-

MAJOR-GENERAL

nuse.   I'm ver-y good at in-te-gral and
fore.   Then I can write a wash-ing bill in

[114]

Slower

3. In fact, when I know what is meant by "mam-e-lon" and "rave-lin"; When I can tell at sight a Mau-ser ri-fle from a jave-lin; When such af-fairs as sor-ties and sur-pris-es I'm more war-y at, And when I know pre-cise-ly what is meant by "com-mis-sar-i-at"; When I have learnt what pro-gress has been

made in mod-ern gun-ner-y; When I know more of tac-tics than a
nov-ice in a nun-ner-y; In short, when I've a smat-ter-ing of
el-e-men-tal strat-e-gy,

Fast again

Yowll
say a bet-ter Ma-jor-Gen-er-al has nev-er sat a gee;

CHORUS

You'll say a bet-ter Ma-jor-Gen-er-al has nev-er sat a gee, You'll

say a bet-ter Ma-jor-Gen-er - al has nev-er sat a gee, You'll

poco a poco cresc.

say a bet-ter Ma-jor-Gen-er - al has nev-er sat a, sat a

gee!

MAJOR-GENERAL

p

4. For my

sf

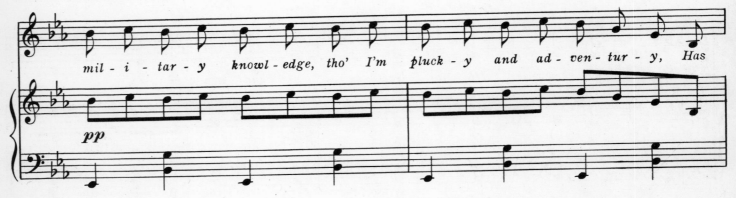

mil - i - tar - y knowl-edge, tho' I'm pluck-y and ad-ven-tur-y, Has

pp

on - ly been brought down to the be - gin-ning of the cen-tu - ry, But

When the Foeman Bares His Steel

MABEL

Go, ____ ye he - roes, go ____ to glo - ry, Though ____ ye die __ in com - bat gor - - y, Ye ____ shall live in song ____ and sto - ry. Go ____ to im - mor - tal - i - ty! Go to death, ___ and go to slaugh - ter; Die, ____ and ev - 'ry Cor - nish daugh - ter With her tears your grave shall wa - - ter! Go __ ye he - roes, go and

die! Go, ye he-roes, go_ and die! Go, ye he-roes, go_ and die! Tho' to

us it's ev-i-dent, Ta-ran-ta-ra, ta-ran-ta-ra! These at-ten-tions are well meant, Ta-ran-ta-

ra! Such ex-pres-sions don't ap-pear, Ta-ran-ta-ra, ta-ran-ta-ra! Cal-cu-

lat-ed men to cheer, Ta-ran-ta-ra! Who are going to meet their fate In a

high-ly nerv-ous state, Ta-ran-ta-ra, ta-ran-ta-ra, ta-ran-ta-ra! Still to

us it's ev-i-dent These at-ten-tions are well meant. Ta-ran-ta - ra, ta-ran-ta-ra, ta-ran-ta-

ra!

EDITH

Go ___ and do your best ___ en-deav - our,

And ___ be-fore all links we sev - er, We ___ will say fare -

well ___ for-ev - er. Go to glo - ry and the grave!

CHORUS of GIRLS

Go to glo - ry and the grave! For your foes are fierce and ruth-less, False, un-

mer-ci-ful, and truth-less. Young and ten-der, old and tooth-less, All in vain their mer-cy crave!

SERG.

We ob-serve too great a stress On the

risks that on us press, And of ref-er-ence a-lack To our chance of com-ing back; Still, per-

haps it would be wise Not to carp or crit-i-cise, For it's ver-y ev-i-dent These at-

POLICE

ten-tions are well meant. Yes, it's ver-y ev-i-dent These at-ten-tions are well meant, Ev-i-

[125]

tears   your grave   shall   wa -   ter.   Go,— ye   he-roes, go and

die!   Go, ye he - roes, go to   im-mor-tal - i - ty!   Go ye

he - roes, go to   im-mor-tal - i - ty! Tho' ye die in com-bat gor-y, Ye shall

live in song and sto - ry; Go to   im - mor-tal - i - ty!

Ah, Leave Me Not to Pine

la, la, la! He loves thee, he is here. Fal - la, la, la, Fal - la!"

FREDERIC

Ah, must I leave thee here In end - less night to dream, Where joy is dark and drear, And sor-

- row all su-preme! Where na-ture, day by day, Will sing,—— in al - tered

tone, This wea - ry roun - de - lay: "He loves thee, he is gone. Fal-

la, la, la, Fal - la, la, la! He loves thee, he is gone. Fal - la, la, la, Fal la!"

FRED (upper note)

MABEL (lower note)

A Policeman's Lot Is Not a Happy One

Moderately fast

SERGEANT

CHORUS of POLICE   SERG.

1. When a fel-on's not en-gaged in his em-ploy-ment (his em-ploy-ment), Or ma-
2. When the en-ter-pris-ing burg-lar's not a-burg-ling (not a-burg-ling), When the

CHORUS   SERG.

tur-ing his fe-lo-nious lit-tle plans (lit-tle plans), His ca-pac-i-ty for in-no-cent en-
cut-throat is-n't oc-cu-pied in crime ('pied in crime), He loves to hear the lit-tle brook a-

CHORUS   SERG.   CHORUS   SERG.

joy-ment ('cent en-joy-ment) Is just as great as an-y hon-est man's (hon-est man's). Our
gur-gling (brook a-gur-gling) And lis-ten to the mer-ry vil-lage chime (vil-lage chime).When the

feel-ings we with dif - fi - cul-ty smoth-er ('cul-ty smoth-er) When con - stab-u-lar-y du-ty's to be
cos-ter's fin-ished jump-ing on his moth-er (on his moth-er), He loves to lie a-bask-ing in the

done (to be done). Ah, take one con-sid-er-a-tion with an-oth-er (with an-oth-er), A po-
sun (in the sun).

lice-man's lot is not a hap-py one. Ah, When con - stab-u - lar-y du-ty's to be

done, to be done, A po - lice-man's lot is not a hap-py one, hap-py one.

one, hap-py one!

With Catlike Tread

PIRATES

So stealth-i - ly the pi - rate creeps, While all the house-hold sound - ly sleeps.

Come, friends, who plough the sea,

Truce to nav - i - ga - tion, Take an-oth - er sta - tion; Let's var - y pi - ra - cee

With a lit - tle bur - gla - ree! Come, friends, who plough the sea,

Truce to nav - i - ga - tion, Take an-oth - er sta - tion; Let's var - y

pi - ra - cee, With a lit - tle bur - gla - ree!

SAMUEL

Here's your— crow-bar and— your— cen - tre-bit, Your

life _____ pre - serv - er, you may want to hit.

Your si - lent match-es, your dark lan - tern seize!—

Police   PIRATES

Take your file——— and your skel-e - ton-ic keys! Ta-ran-ta-ra! With cat-like

Police   PIRATES

tread, Ta-ran-ta-ra! In si-lence dread.   With

cat - like tread Up - on our prey we steal, In si - lence dread Our

cau-tious way we feel! No sound at all, We nev-er speak a word; A

fly's foot - fall Would be dis - tinct - ly heard! Come, friends, who

plough the sea, Truce to nav - i - ga - tion, Take an-oth - er sta - tion;

Let's var - y pi - ra - cee_____ With a lit - tle bur - gla -

ree! With cat - like tread Up - on our prey we

steal, In si - lence dread Our cau - tious way we

feel!

PATIENCE
OR
Bunthorne's Bride

PATIENCE

OR

Bunthorne's Bride

WITH the American productions of *The Pirates* safely launched, Sullivan had once more resumed the role of serious composer. He had been commissioned to compose a sacred cantata for the forthcoming Leeds Festival and chose as his text *The Martyr of Antioch*, a poem by Dean Milman. In its original state it was purely narrative in form and needed to be broken up into the series of solos and choruses that the cantata form demands. Accordingly, he invited Gilbert to make the new version. Gilbert, who liked nothing better than to be taken seriously as a poet, was, of course, delighted and turned out the libretto in short order. The cantata was a tremendous success at Leeds, and the critics were all too ready to point out what a pity it was that so distinguished a composer should waste his time and talents on such trivia as operettas. Gilbert's stage experience was evident in the text, which was rather more dramatic than the usual run of cantatas. In fact, the Carl Rosa Opera Company revived *The Martyr* in a stage version, in 1898, and took it on a profitable tour of the provinces.

Meanwhile, Gilbert had given Sullivan the libretto for their next operetta, and the latter carried it with him on a trip to the Riviera that he took during the winter months of 1880-81. He returned to England in February, in time to be in on the winning of an injunction suit that he, Gilbert, and Carte had brought against the directors of The Comedy Opera Company. From then on, the three had exclusive control of all the operettas. Incidentally, Gilbert and Sullivan worked with Carte, not on a royalty basis, but on a profit-sharing agreement. This was a gamble, in as much as they made nothing out of one of their productions until it had made its expenses. On the other hand, not one of their productions ever actually lost money, so that they profited far more than they would have, if they had signed the usual royalty contract.

The new libretto, as Gilbert first planned it, was to be a lampoon of the Pre-Raphaelites and the esthetic movement championed by Oscar Wilde, both of which were attracting wide attention at the moment. Then he was stricken by a recurrent malady of his, a disinclination to do any more work than was absolutely necessary. He decided to make a libretto based on one of his *Bab Ballads*, "The Rival Curates," named his two rivals Reginald Bunthorne and Archibald Grosvenor, and set to work. He had made considerable progress when he began to be assailed by doubts. There had been considerable criticism of his handling of Dr. Daly, the curate in *The Sorcerer*. Lewis Carroll, in particular, had been horrified by the song about "the pale young curate," which, he thought, held the clergy up to ridicule. If, now, he wrote an entire operetta about *two* curates, and ridiculous ones to boot, wouldn't there be even more trouble? The decision he reached is contained in a letter that he wrote to Sullivan on November 1, 1880:

"I want to see you particularly about the new piece. Although it is two-thirds finished, I don't feel comfortable about it. I feel hampered by the restrictions which the nature of the subject places upon the freedom of my action, and I want to revert to my old idea of rivalry between two aesthetic fanatics. . . . I entertained this idea at first, as you may remember, but abandoned it because I foresaw great difficulty in getting the chorus to dress and make up aesthetically. But if we can get du Maurier to design the costumes, I don't know that the difficulty will be insuperable."

Whether or not du Maurier did design the costumes I have been unable to discover. At all events, Gilbert abandoned his rival curates and cast about for two characters that would fit the general plan of the story. He found the ideal Bunthorne in Oscar Wilde, who, although he was only twenty-five years old at the time, had already achieved the distinction of being caricatured in *Punch* and was rapidly becoming famous for his velvet coat and knee breeches and his desire to live up to his blue china. As the prototype of Grosvenor he chose Algernon Swinburne, who, although a less spectacular poseur than Wilde, was the current symbol of the Pre-Raphaelite movement. Sullivan, waiting until the last minute as usual, finally got to work on the music in March, finishing the score barely in time for the opening, which took place on the evening of April 23, 1881. The new piece was entitled, *Patience; or, Bunthorne's Bride*, "an entirely new and original aesthetic opera in two acts," and presented the following cast:

Reginald Bunthorne	*Major Murgatroyd*
George Grossmith	Frank Thornton
Archibald Grosvenor	*Duke of Dunstable*
Rutland Barrington	Durward Lely
Mr. Bunthorne's Solicitor	*Lady Angela*........Jessie Bond
George Rowley	*Lady Saphir*....Julia Gwynne
Colonel Calverley	*Lady Ella*........Miss Fortescue
Richard Temple	*Lady Jane*..........Alice Barnett
	Patience.....Leonora Braham

Grossmith, who was short and slight, was made up as Oscar Wilde, while the fleshy and ponderous Barrington impersonated the tiny Swinburne. The piece was a success from the beginning—in fact, it ran exactly one year and seven months.

Carte, meanwhile, was preparing to bestow upon the pair a distinction that had hitherto been enjoyed only by Richard Wagner—a theater built for the exclusive production of their works. He had bought land in the center of London, in the neighborhood of the Savoy chapel and near the site of the palace of John of Gaunt, and there erected a house that was the last word in theatrical architecture. For one thing, it was the first London theater to be entirely lighted by electricity—although Carte reassured the more timid customers by announcing that gas was also laid in and that the center light of the auditorium could be gaslit at a moment's notice, in case of a breakdown of the electric system. In opening the new house, Carte was the first London manager to abolish the extra-fee system (under which you tip the usher for showing you to your seat), a system that prevails in France to this day. He also established the "queue" line for persons wishing to buy the unreserved seats.

The new theater, which he named The Savoy, opened on the tenth of October, 1881, with *Patience*, which he had moved over from the Opéra Comique. The house seated 1292 persons and with a reasonably full attendance would yield about $1300 a performance, twice the amount needed to keep the show running. That meant that the "nut" of a Gilbert and Sullivan Savoy production, the amount needed to clear expenses, was something over five thousand dollars a week. A contemporary musical show frequently costs four times that sum—and it isn't by Gilbert and Sullivan, either.

THE STORY

ACT I

In front of Castle Bunthorne, a number of young maidens, handsomely attired in esthetic draperies, are playing on lutes and advertising the fact that they are TWENTY LOVE-SICK MAIDENS WE. All are enthralled by one Reginald Bunthorne, a fleshly poet. Among them, Lady Jane alone is old enough to know about such things and realizes that the object of their affections happens to be enamored of Patience, the village milkmaid. Unspoiled, healthy, and happy child that she is, Patience believes that people in love never seem quite well, and astonishes the maidens by admitting that I CANNOT TELL WHAT THIS LOVE MAY BE.

The maidens find this difficult to understand, for they have always been in love. A year ago, in fact, they were all engaged to the Thirty-fifth Dragoon Guards. And now these fleshly men of full habit, these doughty soldiers of the queen, march in, followed by their Colonel, who promptly enlightens everyone, with IF YOU WANT A RECEIPT for that popular mystery, as to just what a heavy dragoon is. But, alas, they are no competition for Reginald Bunthorne, who enters at that moment, seemingly engrossed in composing a poem (though he hears plainly all they say, "twenty love-sick maidens they"). He reads his poem, stating that to understand it it is necessary for all to cling passionately to one another and think of faint lilies.

The maidens continue to trail wistfully after Bunthorne, and the Colonel voices the thoughts of the disappointed dragoons when he states that he had thought no lady could resist him, WHEN I FIRST PUT THIS UNIFORM ON.

Bunthorne, left alone, confesses that his medievalism's affectation is born of a morbid love of admiration and proffers some splendid advice as to what to do IF YOU'RE ANXIOUS FOR TO SHINE in the high esthetic line.

He then makes poetic advances to Patience, who is not at all responsive. The maidens tell Patience that love is a duty and must be completely unselfish; whereupon she decides to fall in love immediately. Her reveries are happily interrupted by the appearance of Archibald Grosvenor, also a poet, but an idyllic one, who loses no time in inquiring, PRITHEE, PRETTY MAIDEN, will you marry me? As Patience does not recognize him, he reminds her that he is the little boy she loved fifteen years before.

Meanwhile, on the advice of his solicitor, Reginald Bunthorne has put himself up to be raffled for, but just as the raffle is about to begin, Patience horrifies the love-sick maidens by volunteering to marry Bunthorne. She has reasoned that since she considers Archibald perfect and believes that she can only love *unselfishly* a man for whom she has no desire whatsoever, selfish or otherwise, that man had better be Reginald. The maidens hasten to transfer their affections to the dragoons, and everything would be all right except for the fact that Archibald Grosvenor chooses this moment to enter, and all twenty of the maidens promptly transfer their affections to *him*.

ACT II

Lady Jane, leaning on a violoncello, decides to remain steadfast to Reginald although all the rest of the fickle crew have deserted him. But she feels that he ought to marry her quickly, since she is not getting younger; in fact, SILVERED IS THE RAVEN HAIR. Archibald enters, followed, as is now usual, by the maidens, who rapturously adore him. But his heart is elsewhere—with Patience, to be exact. He attempts to console them with the fable of THE MAGNET AND THE CHURN. But this fails, and even Patience herself is miserable beyond descrip-tion. Her education has advanced. She now realizes that LOVE IS A PLAINTIVE SONG, her dilemma being that, while she adores Archibald, she thinks it her duty to marry his rival, Reginald.

The rival poets are by this time mutually consumed with jealousy. Reginald demands that Archibald cease being esthetic and Archibald finally agrees, while Reginald boasts how all the ladies follow WHEN I GO OUT OF DOOR. He is so thoroughly delighted with his triumph over Archibald that he decides to be a reformed character and never again be his former unpleasant self. Hearing this, Patience naturally comes to the conclusion that since there would be nothing unselfish in loving such a perfect being, she can now become Archibald's, since Archibald, by the terms of his agreement with Reginald, has become a commonplace young man, a matter-of-fact young man, a steady and stolid-y, jolly Bank-holiday everyday young man.

Reginald is crushed. Lady Jane marries one of the officers of the dragoons, and poor Reginald, crushed again, decides that—

> *In that case unprecedented,*
> *Single I must live and die—*
> *I shall have to be contented*
> *With a tulip or lily!*

Twenty Love-Sick Maidens We

I Cannot Tell What This Love May Be

Lightly and gracefully

PATIENCE

I can-not tell what this love may
If love is a thorn, they show no

be That com-eth to all, but not to me; It can-not be kind as they'd im-
wit Who fool-ish-ly hug and fost-er it. If love is a weed, how sim-ple

ply, Or why do these la - dies sigh? It can-not be joy and rap - ture
they Who gath-er it day by day! If love is a net-tle that makes you

deep, Or why do these gen - tle la - dies weep? It can-not be bliss - ful as 'tis
smart, Then why do you wear it next your heart? And if it be none of these, say

said,— Or why are their eyes so _____ won-drous red?
I,— Ah, why do you sit and _____ sob and sigh?

rit.
follow the voice
a tempo
mf

Though ev-'ry-where _____ true love I see

A-com-ing to all _____ but not to me, I can-not tell what _____ this love _____ may

rall.

mf *a tempo*

be! _____ For I _____ am blithe and I _____ am gay, While they _____ sit

sigh-ing night _____ and day; For I _____ am blithe and I _____ am gay, Think of the

gulf— 'twixt them— and me. Think of the gulf— 'twixt them— and

me, Fal - la-la-la - la, la-la-la-la-la-la-la-la - la, la-la-la-la-la-la-la-la-la-

1.

la, and mi - - se - rie! espr.

2.

la, and mi - se - rie!

If You Want a Receipt

yes, yes, yes, yes, yes! Take
all the re-mark-a-ble peo-ple in his-to-ry, Rat-tle them off to a
pop-u-lar Chorus: Yes, yes, yes, yes,
yes, yes, yes!

1. The
(2. If you)

pluck of Lord Nel-son on board of the Vic-to-ry, Ge-nius of Bis-marck de-
want a re-ceipt for this sol-dier-like par-a-gon, Get at the wealth of the

staccato

Nar - ra - tive pow - ers of Dick - ens and Thac - ke - ray, Vic - tor Em - man - u - el
Skill of Sir Gar - net in thrash - ing a can - ni - bal, Fla - vour of Ham - let, the

poco cresc.

peak-haunt-ing Po - ve - ril, Thom - as A - qui - nas, And Doc - tor Sa - che - ve - rell,
Strang-er, a touch of him, Lit - tle of Man - fred (but not ver - y much of him),

più cresc.

Tup - per and Ten - ny - son, Dan - iel De - foe, An - tho - ny Trol - lope and
Bea - dle of Bur - ling - ton, Ri - chard - son's show, Mis - ter Mi - caw - ber and

Mis - ter Gui - zot! _____
Ma - dame Tus - saud! _____   Ah! _____

Chorus Yes,   yes,   yes,   yes,   yes,   yes,

f deciso

[150]

When I First Put This Uniform On

In a spirited march tempo

COLONEL

1. When I first put this u‑ni‑form
(2. I) said, when I first put it

on, I said, as I looked in the glass,
on, "It is plain to the ver‑i‑est dunce,

"It's one to a mil‑lion That
That ev‑er‑y beau‑ty Will

an‑y ci‑vil‑ian My fig‑ure and form will sur‑pass.
feel it her du‑ty To yield to its glam‑our at once.

Gold lace has a charm for the
They will see that I'm free‑ly gold‑

fair, And I've plen-ty of that, and to spare, While a lov-er's pro-fes-sions, When
laced In a u - ni-form hand-some and chaste." But the per - i - pa - tet - ics Of

ut - tered in Hes-sians, Are el - o-quent ev-'ry - where!" A_ fact that I count-ed up-
long-haired aes-thet-ics Are ver-y much more to their taste, Which I nev-er count-ed up-

CHORUS

on, When I first put this u - ni-form on! By a sim - ple coon, When I first put this u - ni-form on! By a sim - ple co-

in - ci - dence, few Could ev - er have count-ed up-on, The same thing oc-curred to
in - ci - dence, few Could ev - er have count-ed up-on, I did-n't an - tic - i - pate

1. COLONEL 2.

me, When I first put this u - ni-form on! 2. I
that, When I first put this u - ni-form on!

If You're Anxious For to Shine

Gracefully

BUNTHORNE

1. If you're anx-ious for to shine— in the high aes-thet-ic line— as a
(2. Be —) el - o - quent in praise of the ver- y dull old days— which have
(3. Then a) sen - ti - men-tal pas-sion of a ve - ge - ta - ble fash-ion must ex-

man of cul - ture rare, You must get up all the germs— of the
long since passed a - way, And con - vince 'em, if you can,— that the
cite your lan - guid spleen, An at - tach - ment à la Pla - to for a

sempre staccato

tran - scen - den - tal terms— and— plant them ev - 'ry - where. You must
reign of good Queen Anne— was— Cul - ture's palm - iest day. Of—
bash - ful young po - ta - to, or a not - too - French French bean! Though the

[154]

lie up - on the dais - ies and dis - course in nov - el phras - es of your
course you will pooh-pooh— what - ev - er's fresh and new,— and de-
Phi - lis - tines may jos - tle, you will rank as an a - pos - tle in the

com - pli - cat - ed state of mind, The mean - ing does - n't mat - ter if it's
clare it's crude and mean. For Art stopped short in the
high aes - thet - ic band, If you walk down Pic - ca - dil - ly with a

on - ly i - dle chat - ter of a tran - scen - den - tal kind.
cul - ti - vat - ed court of the Em - press Jo - se - phine.
pop - py or a lil - y in your me - di - ae - val hand.

And ev - 'ry one will say, As you walk your mys - tic
And ev - 'ry one will say, As you walk your mys - tic
And ev - 'ry one will say, As you walk your flow - ery

way,   "If— this— young man ex - press-es him - self in
way,   "If— that's not good e - nough— for him which is
way,   "If— he's— con - tent with a ve - ge - ta - ble love which would

terms too deep for me,   Why, what a ver - y sin - gu - lar - ly
good e - nough for me,   Why, what a ver - y cul - ti - vat - ed
cer - tain - ly not suit me,   Why, what a most par - tic - u - lar - ly

deep young man this deep young man must be!"
kind of youth this kind of youth must be!"
pure young man this pure young man must be!"

rit.

f   *a tempo*

1.-2.   *p*   3.

2. Be—
3. Then a

p   *sf*

[156]

Prithee, Pretty Maiden

Very tenderly and rather slow — GROSVENOR

1. Pri-thee, pret-ty maid-en,
2. Pri-thee, pret-ty maid-en,

pri-thee, tell me true. (Hey, but I'm dole-ful, wil-low, wil-low wa-ly!)
will you mar-ry me? (Hey, but I'm hope-ful, wil-low, wil-low wa-ly!)

Have you e'er a lov-er a-dang-ling af-ter you? Hey, wil-low wa-ly O!
I may say at once, I'm a man of pro-per-tee, Hey, wil-low wa-ly O!

I would fain dis-cov-er If you have a lov-er! Hey,— wil-low wa-ly— O!
Mon-ey, I des-pise it; Man-y peo-ple prize it, Hey,— wil-low wa-ly— O!

Silvered Is the Raven Hair

Moderately slow tempo

JANE

Sil - vered is the ra - ven hair, Spread - ing is the part - ing straight,
Fad - ing is the ta - per waist, Shape - less grows the shape - ly limb,

Mot - tled the com - plex - ion fair, Halt - ing is the youth - ful gait,
And al - though se - vere - ly laced, Spread - ing is the fi - gure trim!

Hol - low is the laugh - ter free, Spec - ta - cled the lim - pid eye,
Stout - er than I used to be, Still more cor - pu - lent grow I,

Lit - tle will be left_ of_ me In the com - ing bye and bye!
There will be too much of_ me In the com - ing bye and bye!

Lit - tle will be left of me In the com - ing_ bye and bye!

There will be too much of me In the com - ing_ bye and

bye!

The Magnet and the Churn

Gaily

GROSVENOR

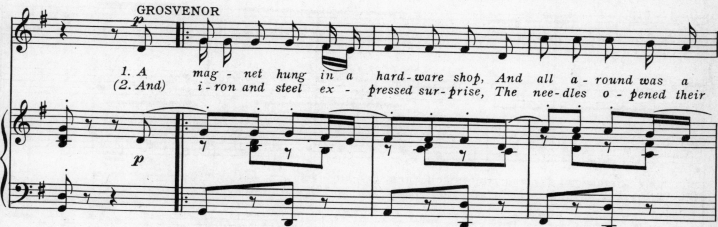

1. A mag - net hung in a hard-ware shop, And all a - round was a
(2. And) i - ron and steel ex - pressed sur-prise, The nee-dles o - pened their

lov - ing crop Of scis-sors and nee - dles, nails and knives, Of - fer - ing love for
well-drilled eyes, The pen - knives felt "shut up," no doubt, The scis-sors de-clared them-

all their lives;   But for
selves "cut out";   The

Love Is a Plaintive Song

Moderately fast

p PATIENCE

1. Love is a plain-tive song, Sung by a suf-f'ring maid, Tell-ing a tale of wrong, Tell-ing of hope be-trayed; Tuned to each chang-ing note, Sor-ry when he is sad,— Mer-ry when he is glad! Mer-ry when he is glad!—

2. Ren-der-ing good for ill, Smil-ing at ev-'ry frown, Yield-ing your own self-will, Laugh-ing your tear-drops down; Nev-er a self-ish whim, Trou-ble or pain to stir;— Ev-er-y-thing for him, Noth-ing at all for her! Noth-ing at all for her!—

rall.

rall. follow the voice

Love that no wrong can cure, Love that is al-ways new, That is the love that's
Love that will aye en-dure, Though the re-wards be few, That is the love that's

pure,—— That is the love—that's true!—— Love that no wrong can cure,
pure,—— That is the love—that's true!—— Love that will aye en-dure,

poco a poco cresc.

Love that is al-ways new,} That is the love— that's pure, That——— is— the
Though the re-wards be few,}

love,— the love— that's true!——

When I Go Out of Door

Very vivaciously

BUNTHORNE

mp stacc.

1. When I go out of
Grosvenor ceive me, if you

door, Of dam-o-zels a score (All sigh-ing and burn-ing, And
can, An ev-'ry-day young man: A com-mon-place type, With a

cling-ing and yearn-ing)Will fol-low me as be-fore. I shall with cul-tured
stick and a pipe, And a half-bred black-and-tan; Who thinks sub-ur-ban

taste Dis-tin-guish gems from paste, And "High did-dle did-dle" Will
"hops" More fun than"Mon-day Pops," Who's fond of his din-ner And

IOLANTHE

OR
The Peer and the Peri

IOLANTHE
OR
The Peer and the Peri

IT WAS obvious, long before *Patience* moved to the Savoy, that its authors need not be in any great hurry to provide something to take its place. Sullivan, accordingly, took one of his customary long vacations, going on a trip, with his friend the Duke of Edinburgh, that took them as far as St. Petersburg (Leningrad to you). There were parties and receptions all along the way—at Copenhagen, Kronstadt, Kiel. At the last-named he was presented to Germany's Prince Wilhelm (later Kaiser Wilhelm II), who promptly sang "I Polished up the Handle of the Big Front Door" for him. *Pinafore*, alias *Amor am Bord*, had been a German favorite for some time.

He returned to London in time to conduct the grand opening performance at the Savoy, and a week later, about October twentieth, received the preliminary sketches for a new piece from Gilbert. This display of energy on his partner's part seems to have exhausted him, for he promptly left for a three months' rest in Egypt. Then, back to London in the spring, in time to celebrate his fortieth birthday, on May 13, 1882.

But a cruel blow awaited him. On the twenty-seventh of that month his mother died. The two had been very close, and his grief at her loss was accentuated by the fact that he, always a devoted family man, was now left utterly alone in the world. His only remaining relatives were his brother's widow and her two children, whose support became his responsibility. One of the children, Herbert Sullivan, he formally adopted.

Some time before, he had met a woman who was to play an important part in his future life, a Mrs. Ronalds, a wealthy American woman and a famous beauty, who was living apart from her husband. After his mother's death, he and Mrs. Ronalds became closer than ever, meeting every day or, if they were separated, exchanging daily telegrams or letters. He even took her to rehearsals and voice trials at the Savoy—which did not make her beloved by the singers. Contemporary opinion insisted that their relationship was wholly platonic. Maybe it was.

To take his mind off the blow of his mother's death Sullivan set to work—very promptly, for him—on the score of the new piece, beginning with the music of the second act. This, an old habit of his, was something more than a trick. The second act of a musical comedy or operetta is generally a comparative low spot —very sound theater, since the first-act finale is a climax, and so necessitates beginning over again in order to work up to the finale of the piece. If, therefore, the composer's brain is not quite warmed up, and the first music he writes is a bit tentative, the very place for it is the opening of Act II, where it won't be noticed. When he gets to the opening of Act I, he is hitting on all twelve, so to speak, and the piece starts off with a bang. I'm not saying that Sullivan's reasoning would have agreed with mine, but at least his practice did.

An added reason for his beginning the new score in the middle was that he didn't like the first act. He sent a message to this effect to Gilbert, and the pair met in Exeter, one day during the summer, for lunch and a conference. By the end of the afternoon they had a new, and mutually satisfactory, first act. At that interview, too, they agreed to reverse their former procedure with *The Pirates:* that is, they would have the official opening in London and send a second company to America for a simultaneous production.

The titles of their last three operettas had begun with the letter *P*, and Gilbert was apparently a bit superstitious about deserting that letter; for he tried three titles for the new piece, all beginning with the lucky initial— *Perola*, *Phyllis*, and *Princess Pearl*. None of them seems to have suited him, for when the new work, the first Gilbert and Sullivan operetta to be written especially for production at the Savoy, opened there on the evening of November 25, 1882, it was called *Iolanthe; or, The Peer and the Peri*, "an entirely new and original fairy opera." The cast was the following:

The Lord Chancellor	*Strephon* ....Richard Temple
George Grossmith	*Queen of the Fairies*
The Earl of Mountararat	Alice Barnett
Rutland Barrington	*Iolanthe*...............Jessie Bond

Earl Tolloller....Durward Lely	Celia............Miss Fortescue
Private Willis	Leila...............Julia Gwynne
Charles Manners	Fleta.................Sybil Grey
	Phyllis........Leonora Braham

(There was also a trainbearer to the Lord Chancellor, a silent role, the archetype of the Mikado's more famous umbrella holder.)

Sullivan's run of ill fortune was not yet over. On the very day of the opening, he received notice that the brokerage firm of Cooper, Hall & Company, to whom he had entrusted everything that he had saved, had gone bankrupt. When he stepped into the orchestra pit that night at the Savoy, it was with the knowledge that, outside his current bank balance of a few hundred pounds, he was penniless. But one of Sullivan's haunts was Monte Carlo; he was an ardent gambler. From his demeanor, no one in the house would have suspected what had happened to him. Icy cool, he concentrated upon the score on the desk before him. *Iolanthe had to be a success.*

And it was a success—no *Pinafore*, perhaps, it nevertheless ran for a year and two months. There were dissenting voices, however, among the critics. *Punch* called it "not within a mile of *Pinafore* or a patch on *Patience*." Moreover, after its initial run it was never as popular in repertory as several of the other Savoy operas. Even Arthur Lawrence, referring to the death of Sullivan's mother, remarks that "under the circumstances it is not surprising that at that time nothing of first-rate importance appeared from his pen. *Iolanthe* and *Princess Ida* are amongst the least appreciated of the operas." If he wants to consider *Princess Ida* as being of less than "first-rate importance," one can

hardly quarrel with him, but to put *Iolanthe* in the same category seems hardly fair. To me, at least, *Iolanthe* ranks with *Pinafore* and *The Mikado* as representing the peak of Gilbert and Sullivan. The score seems to me one of the most spontaneous and ingratiating that Sullivan ever wrote, harmonically much more colorful than most of them and offering more rhythmic variety. Incidentally, Lawrence's attributing his alleged slump to the death of his mother is an ill-founded assumption. Sullivan shares at least one attribute with Mozart: the composer in him functioned independently of the man. If mental depression and physical pain (and he was a lifelong sufferer from both) could have affected his creative powers, most of the Savoy operas would never have been written.

Gilbert, too, is at his best in *Iolanthe*. The main idea —that of a hero who is the son of a fairy and a peer, and is therefore half fay, half human—was a good one when it was a *Bab Ballad*; it is even better when embodied in a libretto. The development of this idea is a brilliant example of Gilbert's genius for basing a grimly logical argument on a preposterous major premise. Nowhere in the entire Savoy repertoire are Gilbert's lyrics defter in rhyme or more captivating in meter. Fifteen years ago, when Winthrop Ames undertook his unforgettable series of Gilbert and Sullivan productions, his initial choice was *Iolanthe*; and the rapturous welcome she received was fresh evidence of the fact that though, as some complain, Gilbert's characters are never quite human, they share one attribute with all the Little People who have no souls: they do not die.

THE STORY

ACT I

Through an Arcadian landscape a group of delightful winged young ladies are tripping hither, tripping thither, singing, WE ARE DAINTY LITTLE FAIRIES—which happens to be true. Tiring of this, they sigh wearily because fairy revels have not been up to snuff since Iolanthe, who used to write all their songs and arrange all their dances, was banished by the Fairy Queen for marrying a mortal. Technically, the penalty should have been death, but Iolanthe was a special case.

Touched by their sorrow, the Fairy Queen pardons the wrongdoer, who has been living at the bottom of a stream. She has chosen this watery abode as a handy method of being close to her son, Strephon. The latter is an Arcadian shepherd

who is in love with Phyllis, a ward in chancery. Strephon dances in, playing on a flageolet, rejoices with his mother on her reinstatement, and asks her to join him in a measure expressive of pleasure, for he is to be married today, today.

Phyllis also dances in, also playing on a flageolet, and greets Strephon with a GOOD MORROW, GOOD LOVER. Their marriage is to take place against the wishes of her guardian, the Lord Chancellor, and both are determined that NONE SHALL PART US.

As they leave, a group of imposing tiaraed gentlemen march in and demand that LOUDLY LET THE TRUMPET BRAY, as they are peers of highest rank and station, paragons of legislation. They are accompanied by the Lord Chancellor, who wastes no time in proclaiming that THE LAW IS THE TRUE EMBODIMENT of everything that's excellent. He admits that he is enamored of Phyllis, but since he doubts the propriety of marrying one of his wards, he summons her in the hope that she will choose one of the peers.

Lord Tolloller states flatly that OF ALL THE YOUNG LADIES I KNOW she is the fairest. But Phyllis will have none of him or his tribe, though he begs her to SPURN NOT THE NOBLY BORN. She astonishes all with the news that her heart is already given, and Strephon, entering at that moment, confesses that it is given to him. The peers depart, dignified and stately, and the Lord Chancellor gives Strephon no encouragement whatever, telling him what happened WHEN I WENT TO THE BAR as a very young man.

Phyllis unfortunately sees the beautiful Iolanthe comforting Strephon, and naturally does not believe him when he swears that Iolanthe is his mother. Considering him faithless, she promptly becomes engaged to two of the noblemen.

The Fairy Queen enters with her ladies. It is with difficulty that the Lord Chancellor is able to understand the Queen to be a fairy, from Andersen's library, since he took her for the proprietor of a ladies' seminary. Piqued by this, the Fairy Queen plans to send Strephon to Parliament, where he will make the House sit through the grouse and salmon season and ennoble all the common councilmen. The peers poohpooh this, indicating that YOUNG STREPHON IS THE KIND OF LOUT they do not care a fig about. But then they plead for mercy as their spirits fall with the curtain.

ACT II

In front of Westminster Hall, Private Willis, the sentry, thinks the profound thoughts that a chap thinks WHEN ALL NIGHT LONG a chap remains on sentry-go. Strephon is now a member of Parliament and carries every bill he chooses, proving that fairies have their uses. The noble lords are terrified by his intellect, a commodity which, as they say, was never found in the House of Peers WHEN BRITAIN REALLY RULED THE WAVES. The lady fairies are now in love with the peers, but the Fairy Queen warns them, OH, FOOLISH FAY, that marrying a mortal is a crime. She confesses that she finds Private Willis attractive, but could never think of him matrimonially.

The Lord Chancellor, still madly in love with Phyllis, outlines the situation of the complete insomniac, WHEN YOU'RE LYING AWAKE with a dismal headache. The peers exhort him to remember that FAINT HEART NEVER WON FAIR LADY.

Strephon at last convinces Phyllis that Iolanthe is really his mother, even though, being, like all his female relatives, a fairy, she looks beautiful and seventeen. Phyllis finally understands, and says that whenever she sees Strephon kissing a very young lady she will know it is an elderly relative. "You will?" says Strephon. "Then, Phyllis, I think we shall be very happy!" They decide to wed immediately in order to avoid the obstacles that might arise IF WE'RE WEAK ENOUGH TO TARRY.

The Lord Chancellor, unaware of all this, has just persuaded himself, after severe inward struggle, of the propriety of his marrying Phyllis. When Iolanthe, at the risk of her life, discovers herself to him as his long-lost wife, the Queen is about to condemn her to death when the entire fairy group announces that they have married peers. This faces her with the prospect of having to slaughter the entire company; but the Lord Chancellor cleverly amends the law to read that every fairy shall die who does *not* marry a mortal. She then deftly saves her own life by marrying Private Willis. Wings spread from the shoulders of the peers as the House of Peers changes to the House of Peris.

We Are Dainty Little Fairies

In a light, playful manner, but not fast

CELIA

We are dain-ty lit-tle fair-ies, Ev-er sing-ing, ev-er danc-ing; We in-dulge in our va-gar-ies In a fash-ion most en-tranc-ing. If you ask the spec-ial func-tion Of our nev-er ceas-ing

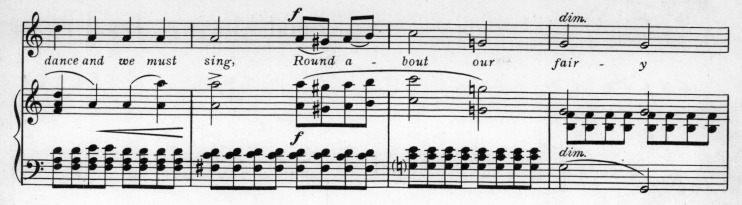

dance and we must sing, Round a - bout our fair - y

ring. We are dain-ty lit - tle fair-ies, Ev - er sing-ing ev - er danc-ing;

We in - dulge in our va - ga-ries In a fash-ion most en - tranc - ing, ____

most en - tranc - ing, ____ most ___ en - tranc - ing.

Trip-ping hith-er, trip-ping thith-er, No-bod-y knows why or whith-er.

Good Morrow, Good Lover

None Shall Part Us

Slowly with much sentiment

Phyllis 1. None shall part us from each oth-er, One in
Strephon 2. All in all since that fond meet-ing When, in

life and death are we: All in all to one an-oth-er, I to
joy, I woke to find Mine the heart, with-in thee beat-ing, Mine the

thee and thou to me! __ All in all to one an-oth-er, I to
love that heart en-shrined! Mine the heart, with-in thee beat-ing, Mine the

Loudly Let the Trumpet Bray

Pompous march tempo

CHORUS

Loud - ly let the trum - pet — bray, Tan - tan - ta - ra, tan - ta - ta - ra!

f marcato

Proud - ly bang the sound - ing — brass - es, —

As up - on its lord - ly — way This u - nique pro - ces - sion — pass - es.

Tan - tan-ta-ra, tan-ta - ra, Tzing,boom,tzing,boom! Tan - ta-ra, tan-ta - ra,Tzing, boom!

Tan - ta - ra, ta ta ta ta ta ta, Tan - ta - ra, ta ta ta ta ta ta,

Tan - ta - ra, ta ta ta ta ta ta, Tan - ta - ra, ta ta ta ta ta ta,

Tan - ta - ra, ta ta ta ta ta ta ta!

Bow, ye low - er mid - dle class - es, Bow, ye trades-men, bow, ye

ponderously

The Law Is the True Embodiment

Vivaciously

LORD CHANCELLOR

1. The Law is the true em-
2. But though the com-pli-
3. And ev - 'ry - one who'd

bod - i - ment Of ev - 'ry-thing that's ex - cel - lent. It
ment im - plied In - flates me with le - gi - ti - mate pride, It
mar - ry a Ward Must come to me for my__ ac - cord, And

has no kind of fault or flaw, And I, my lords, em -
nev - er - the - less can't be de - nied That it has its in - con -
in my court I sit all day, Giv - ing a - gree - a - ble

Of All the Young Ladies I Know

Smoothly, like a Barcarole

Lord Tolloller 1. Of all the young la - dies I

Phyllis 2. I'm ver - y much pain'd to re -

know, ___ This pret - ty young la - dy's the fair - est: Her lips have the ros - i - est

fuse, ___ But I'll stick to my pipes and my ta - bors; I can spell all the words that I

show, ___ Her eyes are the rich - est and rar - est. Her or - i - gin's low - ly, it's

use, ___ And my gram - mar's as good as my neigh - bors. As for birth, I was born like the

true, ___ But of birth and po - si - tion I've plen - ty; I've gram - mar and spell - ing for

rest. ___ My be - hav - iour is rus - tic but heart - y, And I know where to turn for the

two,   And blood and be - hav - iour for twen - ty!   Ah! ____
best, When I want a par - tic - u - lar par - ty!   Ah! ____

mp espressivo

Her or - i - gin's low - ly, it's true, I've gram - mar and
Though my sta - tion is none of the best, I sup - pose ____ I was

poco cresc.

spell - ing for two; Of birth and po - si - tion I've plen - ty, With blood and be - hav - iour for
born like the rest. I know where to look for my heart - y, When I want a par - tic - u - lar

mf ———— *f*

twen - ty! Of birth and po - si - tion I've plen - ty, With blood and be - hav - iour for twen -
par - ty! I know where to look for my heart - y, When - ev - er I want ___ a par -

f follow the voice

1.   *2.*

ty!
ty!

8va ....

dolce
p a tempo

[192]

Spurn Not the Nobly Born

Sustained and with expression

p LORD TOLLOLER

1. Spurn not the no-bly born With love af-fect-ed! Nor treat with vir-tuous scorn The
2. Spare us the bit-ter pain Of stern de-ni-als, Nor with low-born dis-dain Aug-

well_ con-nect-ed! High rank in-volves no shame, We boast an e-qual claim
ment_ our_ tri-als. Hearts just as pure and fair May beat in Bel-grave Square

With him of hum-ble name To be re-spect-ed! Blue blood! Blue blood! When
As in the low-ly air Of Sev-en Di-als! Blue blood! Blue blood! Of

vir-tuous love is sought, Thy pow'r is_ naught, Though dat-ing from the Flood, Blue blood, ah, blue blood!
what a-vail art thou To serve_ us_ now? Though dat-ing from the Flood, Blue blood, ah, blue blood!

[193]

When I Went to the Bar

Young Strephon Is the Kind of Lout

Gay march tempo

mf CHORUS

Girls: With Strephon for your
Men: Young Strephon is the

foe, no doubt, A fear - ful pros - pect o - pens out! And who shall say What
kind of lout We do not care a fig a - bout! We can - not say What

e - vils may Re - sult in con - se - quence? A hid - eous ven - geance
e - vils may Re - sult in con - se - quence. But lord - ly ven - geance

will pur - sue All no - ble - men who ven - ture to Op - pose his views, Or
will pur - sue All kinds of com - mon peo - ple who Op - pose our views, Or

GIRLS

high pres-tige. (The word "pres-tige" is French, The word "pres-tige" is

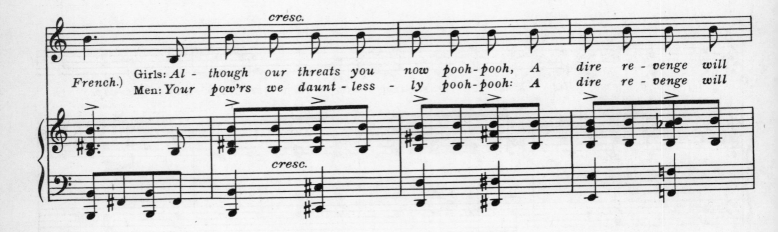

French.) Girls: Al - though our threats you now pooh-pooh, A dire re - venge will
Men: Your pow'rs we daunt-less - ly pooh-pooh: A dire re - venge will

fall on you. With Stre - phon for your foe, no doubt, A fear - ful pros - pect
fall on you. Young Stre - phon is the kind of lout We do not care a

o - pens out! And who shall say What e - vils may Re - sult in con - se - quence?
fig a - bout! We can - not say What e - vils may Re - sult in con - se - quence.

When All Night Long

Moderately

PRIVATE WILLIS

1. When
(2. When)

all night long a chap re - mains On sen - try - go, to chase mo -
in that House M. P.'s di - vide, If they've a brain and cer - e -

not - o - ny He ex - er - cis - es of his brains, That
bel - lum, too, They've got to leave that brain out - side, And

is, as - sum - ing that he's got an - y. Tho' nev - er nur - tur'd
vote just as their lead - ers tell 'em to. But then the pros - pect

in the lap Of lux-u-ry, Yet I ad-mon-ish you, I am an in-tel-
of a lot Of dull M. P's in close prox-im-i-ty, All think-ing for them-

lec-tual chap, And think of things that would as-ton-ish you. I
selves, is what No man can face with e-qua-nim-i-ty. Then

A little more animated

oft-en think it's com-i-cal Fal, lal,— la! Fal, lal,— la! How
let's re-joice with loud Fal, lal, Fal, lal,— la! Fal, lal,— la! That

Na-ture al-ways does con-trive, Fal, lal,— la, la! That—

ev-'ry boy and— ev-'ry gal That's born in-to the—

When Britain Really Ruled the Waves

With majesty and grandeur

ff marcato

LORD MOUNTARARAT

mf

1. When Brit-ain real-ly ruled the waves (In
(2.When) Wel-ling-ton thrash'd Bo-na-parte, As
(3. And) while the House of Peers with-holds Its

good Queen Bess-'s ___ time), The House of Peers made no pre-tence To
ev-'ry child can___ tell, The House of Peers, through-out the war, Did
leg-is-la-tive___ hand, And no-ble states-men do not itch To

in-tel-lec-tual em-i-nence, Or scho-lar-ship su-blime; Yet
noth-ing in par-tic-u-lar, And did it ver-y well: Yet
in-ter-fere with mat-ters which They do not un-der-stand, As

Brit - ain won her proud - est bays In good Queen Bess's
Brit - ain set the world a - blaze In good King George's
bright will shine Great Brit - ain's rays As in King George's

glo - rious days! Yet Brit - ain won her proud - est bays In good Queen
glo - rious days! Yet Brit - ain set the world a - blaze In good King
glo - rious days! As bright will shine Great Brit - ain's rays As in King

ff CHORUS

Bess's glo - rious days. Yes, Brit - ain won her proud - est bays In good Queen
George's glo - rious days. Yes, Brit - ain set the world a - blaze In good King
George's glo - rious days. As bright will shine Great Brit - ain's rays As in King

1. - 2.

Bess 's glo - rious days. 2. When
George 's glo - rious days. 3. And

3.

George - 's glo - rious days.

Oh, Foolish Fay

Quietly, in a singing style

f

poco rit

p QUEEN

p a tempo

1. Oh, fool-ish fay, Think you, be-cause His brave ar-
2. On fire that glows With heat in-tense I turn the

ray My bo-som thaws, I'd dis-o-bey Our fair-y
hose Of com-mon sense, And out it goes At small ex-

laws? Be-cause I fly In realms a-bove, In ten-den-
pense! We must main-tain Our fair-y law; That is the

say so! / won-der! Oh, / Oh, am-'rous / Cap-tain dove! / Shaw!

Type of O - vi - dius Na - so! / Type of true love kept un - der! This heart of mine Is / Could thy Bri - gade With

soft as thine, Al - though I dare not say so! / cold cas - cade Quench my great love, I won - der!

When You're Lying Awake

Quick but not too fast   LORD CHANCELLOR

1. When you're
(2. For you)
(3. And)

ly - ing a - wake with a dis - mal head-ache and re - pose is ta - boo'd by anx-
dream you are cross - ing the Chan-nel, and toss-ing a - bout in a steam - er from
he and the crew are on bi - cy - cles too, which they've some-how or oth - er in-

i - e - ty, I con - ceive you may use an - y lan-guage you choose to in-
Har - wich, Which is some - thing be - tween a large bath - ing ma - chine and a
vest - ed in, And he's tell - ing the tars all the par - tic - u - lars of a

dulge in, with - out im - pro - pri - e - ty; For your brain is on fire,___ the
ver - y small sec - ond - class car - riage, And you're giv - ing a treat (pen - ny
com - pa - ny he's in - ter - est - ed in; It's a scheme of de - vic - es, to

bed - clothes con - spire __ of u - su - al slum - ber to plun-der you: First your
ice and cold meat) to a par - ty of friends and re - la - tions; They're a
get at low pric - es, all goods from cough mix - tures to ca - bles (Which

coun - ter - pane goes, and un - cov - ers your toes, and your sheet slips de - mure - ly from
rav - en - ous horde, and they all came on board at Sloane Square and South Ken - sing - ton
tick - led the sail - ors), by treat - ing re - tail - ers as though they were all veg - e -

poco a poco cresc.

un - der you; Then the blank - et - ing tick - les, you feel like mixed pick - les, so
Sta - tions. And bound on that jour - ney you find your at - tor - ney (who
ta - bles; You get a good spades-man to plant a small trades-man (first

poco a poco cresc.

ter - ri - bly sharp is the prick - ing, And you're hot, and you're cross, and you
start - ed that morn - ing from Dev - on); He's a bit un - der - siz'd, and you
take off his boots with a boot - tree), And his legs will take root, and his

tum - ble and toss till there's noth - ing 'twixt you and the tick - ing. Then the
don't feel sur - pris'd when he tells you he's on - ly e - lev - en. Well, you're
fin - gers will shoot, and they'll blos - som and bud like a fruit tree; From the

bed - clothes all creep to the ground in a heap and you pick 'em all up in a
driv - ing like mad with this sing - u - lar lad (by the bye the ship's now a four -
green - gro - cer tree you get grapes and green pea, cau - li - flow - er, pine - ap - ple and

tan - gle; Next your pil - low re - signs and po - lite - ly de - clines to re -
wheel - er), And you're play - ing round games, and he calls you bad names when you
cran - ber - ries, While the pas - try - cook plant cher - ry bran - dy will grant, ap - ple

main at its u - su - al an - gle! Well, you get some re - pose in the
tell him that "ties pay the deal - er"; But this you can't stand, so you
puffs, and three - cor - ners, and ban - bur - ys; The shares are a pen - ny, and

head's on the floor, and you've nee-dles and pins from your soles to your shins, and your flesh is a-creep, for your left leg's a-sleep, and you've cramp in your toes, and a fly on your nose, and some fluff in your lung, and a fev-er-ish tongue, and a thirst that's in-tense, And a gen-er-al sense that you have-n't been sleep-ing in clo - ver; But the

dark - ness has pass'd, and it's day - light at last, and the

cresc.

night has been long, dit - to, dit - to my song,

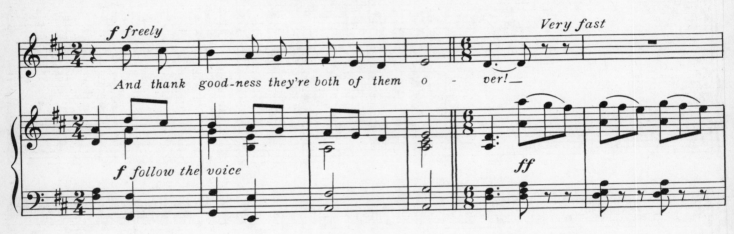

f freely   *Very fast*

And thank good-ness they're both of them o - ver!—

f follow the voice   *ff*

Faint Heart Never Won Fair Lady

nev - er won fair la - dy!" Nev - er, nev - er, nev - er.

"Faint heart nev - er won fair la - dy!"

1. Ev - 'ry jour - ney has an end, When at the
2. While the sun shines make your hay, Where a

worst af - fairs will mend, Dark the dawn when day is
will is, there's a way, Beard the li - on in his

nigh, Hus - tle your horse and don't say die!
lair, None but the brave de - serve the fair!

LORD CHANCELLOR

I'll_ take heart And make a start, Though_ I fear the

pros - pect's shad - y, Much_ I'd spend To gain_ my end:

mf ALL THREE

"Faint heart nev - er won fair la - dy!" Nev - er, nev - er

nev - er. "Faint heart nev - er won fair la - dy!"

Noth - ing ven - ture, noth - ing win;

Blood— is thick, but wa - ter's thin; In for a pen - ny,

in for a pound; It's Love— that makes the world go round!

If We're Weak Enough to Tarry

Joyously

_p_ STREPHON

If we're weak e - nough to tar - ry

Ere we mar - ry, You_ and I, Of the feel - ing I in - spire

You may tire ___ By_ and bye; For peers with flow - ing cof - fers

Press their of - fers, That is why I am sure we should not tar - ry

mp PHYLLIS

Ere we mar - ry, You and I. If we're weak e - nough to tar - ry

mp

Ere we mar - ry, You and I, With a more at - trac - tive maid - en,

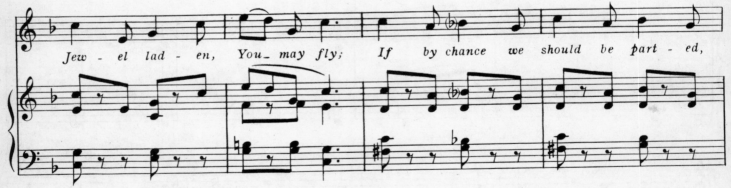

Jew - el lad - en, You may fly; If by chance we should be part - ed,

Bro - ken-heart - ed I should die. So I think we will not tar - ry

PRINCESS IDA
OR
Castle Adamant

PRINCESS IDA

OR
Castle Adamant

IN THE sixth month of *Iolanthe*'s run, on May 4, 1883, Sullivan received a letter, dated the day before, from the Prime Minister. "Dear Mr. Sullivan," it read. "I have the pleasure to inform you that I am permitted by Her Majesty to propose that you should receive the honour of Knighthood, in recognition of your distinguished talents as a composer and of the services which you have rendered to the promotion of the art of music generally in this country. I hope that it may be agreeable to you to accept the proposal. I remain, Faithfully yours, W. Gladstone." Three years earlier, in a conversation with his friend, the Duke of Edinburgh, Sullivan had announced that he didn't want to be knighted, and wouldn't accept a knighthood if it were offered. But a hypothetical refusal is not necessarily the real thing. On May 27 he went, with George Macfarren (who was blind, by the way) and George Grove, to Windsor Castle, where the three were knighted by Queen Victoria.

Gilbert was not there. It is all very well to say that Sullivan's reputation, in musical circles, rested on his serious works in the larger forms. The fact remains that, to the man in the street, he was a national figure on account of the Savoy operas; and the man with whom he had collaborated on seven of them, whose name had been inseparable from his for a dozen years, was Gilbert. If he was overlooked, the neglect must have been calculated, must have been the result of a determination, on the part of England's little group of Serious Thinkers, to belittle the worth of Sullivan's light music and put the emphasis on his more pretentious offerings.

Certainly there is plenty of evidence to support such a suspicion. Shortly after his knighthood had been announced, some incredible ass published an article in the *Musical Review* which started out: "To use a slightly stale expression, *Noblesse oblige* [slightly!], some things Mr. Arthur Sullivan may do, *Sir* Arthur Sullivan ought not to do. In other words, it will look rather more than odd to see announced in the papers that a new comic opera is in preparation, the book by Mr.

W. S. Gilbert and the music by Sir Arthur Sullivan. A musical knight can hardly write shop ballads, either; he must not dare to soil his hands with anything less than an anthem or a madrigal; oratorio, in which he has so conspicuously shone, and symphony, must now be his line." And so on. That same year, Grove, in the third volume of his *Dictionary of Music and Musicians*, wrote that "Surely the time has come when so able and experienced a master of voice, orchestra, and stage effect . . . may apply his gifts to a serious opera on some subject of abiding human or [the distinction is Grove's] national interest."

(Incidentally, in the current edition of *Grove's*, H. Saxe-Wyndham writes that "It is not to be denied that his more serious works, including his oratorios, cantatas, and his one 'grand' opera, have declined in popularity within the last quarter of a century. . . . Meanwhile in ever-increasing circles the fountain of joy which he created sparkles and gushes out to the inexpressible pleasure of a third generation of playgoers whose purest pleasures are found in the delights of 'Savoy' Opera.")

To all of this, Sullivan did not respond—not yet. Meanwhile, Gilbert, whatever his private thoughts on the subject of knighthood may have been, made no public comment, but busied himself with one of life's more pleasant occupations, that of spending money. He built himself a house at No. 39 Harrington Gardens, South Kensington (it used to be a shrine for visiting Savoyards; I wonder if it is still standing). It was an imposing edifice, with his family arms and crest over the doorway and fairly reeking, inside, with paneled walls, beamed ceilings, stained-glass windows, electric light, central heating, a bathroom on every floor, and—a telephone. He rented another house in the country, "Breakspears," where he spent the summer playing much tennis. He was very tall, with a tremendous reach, and found a good deal of difficulty in keeping the ball inside the court. A lesser man would have gone meekly to work to practice shortening his strokes, but not Gilbert. He had the court lengthened.

In the intervals of tennis and housebuilding he found

time to work on another libretto for Sullivan—three, in fact. The first was an adaptation of a fairy play of his, *The Wicked World*. There had been a certain amount of grumbling in the papers to the effect that he was going in too heavily for potions, and supernatural beings, and such. This seems hardly fair. *Patience*, *The Pirates*, and *Pinafore* certainly had nothing supernatural about them. We have to go back to *The Sorcerer* to find any magic before *Iolanthe*. Nevertheless, Carte seems to have taken the criticisms to heart, for he intimated that it might be a good idea to give fairyland a rest for a while. Nothing daunted, he came through with another idea, concerning a magic lozenge. Sullivan rejected this one, although, as you will see later, he was destined to encounter it again. Whereupon Gilbert reached down into the barrel once more, coming up with *The Princess*, a blank-verse parody of Tennyson's poem that he had written in 1870. Except for turning certain speeches and scenes into song lyrics he left the original much as it had been, blank verse and all, and Sullivan consented to set it to music. The result, *Princess Ida; or, Castle Adamant*, was presented at the Savoy on the evening of January 5, 1884, with the following cast:

King Hildebrand	*Princess Ida*
Rutland Barrington	Leonora Braham
Hilarion..................H. Bracy	*Lady Blanche*
King Gama	Rosina Brandram
George Grossmith	*Lady Psyche*.......Kate Chard
Cyril...............Durward Lely	*Melissa*.................Jessie Bond
Florian............Charles Ryley	*Sacharissa*............Sybil Grey
Arac.............Richard Temple	*Chloe*...........Miss Heathcote
Guron..........Warwick Gray	*Ada*.....................Lilian Carr
Scynthius...............Mr. Lugg	

(*Princess Ida* is the only one of the Savoy operas to be written in three acts.)

Fate seemed to have conspired to make the weeks preceding any new Savoy production ones of trouble and unhappiness for Sullivan. In December, 1883, his old friend, the composer Frederick Clay, suffered two paralytic strokes, and the news affected Sullivan so deeply that he had to stop work for several days. Moreover, the shock brought on another of his old attacks, so that he worked under a double handicap. With only a fortnight left before the opening he labored night and day, finishing the score only three days before the final dress rehearsal. On the day of the opening he was suffering such pain and exhaustion that the doctor gave him an injection of morphine and forbade him to conduct. At seven that evening he had another injection, dressed, went to the theater, and staggered into the orchestra pit. The frantic ovation that he had from the audience revived him a bit, and he managed successfully to conduct the performance, but fainted after the curtain call, and had to be carried home.

He had done his part well, but Gilbert had not. As a libretto, *Princess Ida* turned out to have practically no action at all, aside from a fight in the last act that came too late to stir things up. Only the lyrics, and Sullivan's music, were up to standard. It was the weakest of the series, to date.

THE STORY

When IDA WAS A TWELVEMONTH OLD she was betrothed to Prince Hilarion, the two-year-old son of King Hildebrand. On the day that the Prince comes of age, he, his father, and their courtiers are watching through telescopes and opera glasses for the arrival of the bride and her highly unprepossessing father, King Gama, and are most annoyed when he arrives minus his daughter. Unable to comprehend why his attractions are not clear to everyone, he offers to present the picture of his true benevolence IF YOU GIVE ME YOUR ATTENTION. More important, he explains that Princess Ida now rules a woman's university at Castle Adamant, where, with one hundred other lovely female intellectuals, she has forsworn wicked man; and where the very thought of marriage is forbidden.

King Gama does hold out the hope to Prince Hilarion that she may relent. The Prince loses no time in going off with his companions to storm Castle Adamant (and Princess Ida's heart) with EXPRESSIVE GLANCES as their lances, while Gama remains behind as hostage.

The beautiful bluestockings are studying both the classics and the villainy of man at the university. Two of the girls have already been expelled for playing with chess*men*, and, even worse, sketching a perambulator. Hilarion and his friends matriculate, disguised, of course, as women. Good as the disguises are, they are finally penetrated, when Cyril, becoming tipsy, sings an old song, WOULD YOU KNOW THE KIND OF MAID?, and the unhappy youths are marched off in chains. Hilarion's father, King Hildebrand, batters down the university gate and rushes in to declare that if Ida doesn't agree to marry his son, he and his soldiers will deal extremely harshly with her university and her three brothers.

Ida defiantly elects to defend her citadel of female instruction. For a while the ladies of Castle Adamant struggle valiantly with battle-axes (they don't use rifles because they might go off); but at last Ida agrees to let her three brothers battle it out with Hilarion and his two friends. Hilarion's side wins, hands down, and Ida resigns her post to accept Hilarion.

Ida Was a Twelvemonth Old

Moderately

HILARION

1. I - da was a twelve - month old, Twen - ty years a -
2. Still, I was a ti - ny Prince Twen - ty years a -

go! I was twice her age, I'm told,
go. She has gain'd up - on me, since

Twen - ty years a - go! Hus - band — twice — as —
Twen - ty years a - go! Though she's — twen - ty -

old— as— wife
one,— it's— true,

Ar - gues— ill for— mar - ried— life;
I — am— bare-ly— twen-ty-two,

cresc.

Bale - ful— proph - e - cies— were— rife,
False— and— fool - ish— proph -ets— you,

mf poco rit

Twen - ty years a -
Twen - ty years a -

mf poco rit

go,
go,

Twen - ty years a - go!
Twen - ty years a - go!

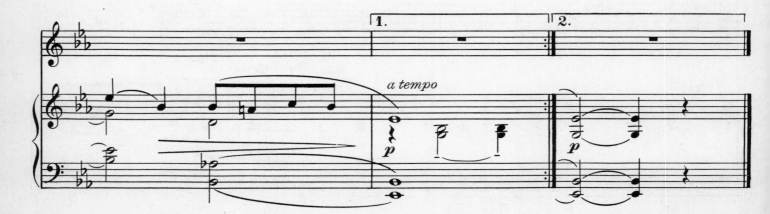

a tempo

1.   **2.**

If You Give Me Your Attention

Quick but not too fast

GAMA

1. If you give me your at-ten-tion, I will tell you what I am: I'm a
(2. To) com-pli-ments in-flat-ed I've a with-er-ing re-ply; And
(3. I'm) sure I'm not as-cet-ic; I'm as pleas-ant as can be; You'll

gen-u-ine phi-lan-thro-pist, all oth-er kinds are sham. Each
van-i-ty I al-ways do my best to mor-ti-fy; A
al-ways find me read-y with a crush-ing re-par-tee. I've an

lit-tle fault of tem-per and each so-ci-al de-fect In my
char-i-ta-ble ac-tion I can skil-ful-ly dis-sect; And
ir-ri-tat-ing chuck-le, I've a cel-e-brat-ed sneer, I've an

err - ing fel - low crea - tures, I en - deav - our to cor - rect. To
in - ter - est - ed mo - tives I'm de - light - ed to de - tect; To I know
en - ter - tain - ing snig - ger, I've a fas - ci - nat - ing leer. To

all their lit - tle weak - ness - es I o - pen peo - ple's eyes; And
ev - 'ry - bod - y's in - come and what ev - 'ry - bod - y earns; And I
ev - 'ry - bod - y's prej - u - dice I know a thing or two; I can

lit - tle plans to snub the self - suf - fi - cient I de - vise; I
care - ful - ly com - pare it with the in - come - tax re - turns; But to
tell a wom - an's age in half a min - ute, and I do. But al -

love my fel - low crea - tures, I do all the good I can,
ben - e - fit hu - man - i - ty how - ev - er much I plan, } Yet
though I try to make my - self as pleas - ant as I can,

[228]

ev - 'ry - bod - y says I'm such a dis - a - gree - able man! And I

1.-2.

can't think why!

2. To
3. I'm

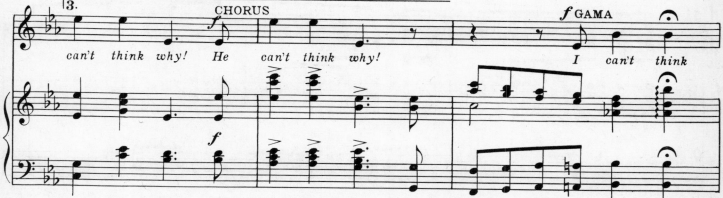

3.

CHORUS

f GAMA

can't think why! He can't think why! I can't think

why!

Expressive Glances

vi - o - let! Oh, gen - tle heigh - o - let (Or lit - tle sigh). On sweet ur -

ban - i - ty, Tho' mere in - an - i - ty, To touch their van - i - ty We will re -

pCYRIL

ly!___ When day is fad - ing, With ser - e - nad - ing And such fri -

vol - i - ty We'll prove our qual - i - ty. A sweet pro - fu - sion Of soft al -

lu - sion This bold in - tru - sion shall jus - ti - fy, This bold in -

Would You Know the Kind of Maid

Hang her head in modest way,
Mine the blush-ing rose of May,
With pout-ing lips,— with pout-ing
lips— that seem to say, "Oh, kiss me, kiss me, kiss me, kiss me,
Though I— die of shame-a!" Please you, that's the kind of maid Sets— my heart a-
flame-a! "Kiss me, kiss me, kiss me, kiss me, Though I— die of
shame-a!" Please you, that's the kind of maid Sets— my heart a-flame-a!

THE MIKADO

OR
The Town of Titipu

THE MIKADO

OR
The Town of Titipu

 T WAS early spring of 1884. *Princess Ida* had been running for three months at the Savoy; and while it was not a failure (Gilbert and Sullivan never had a complete failure in the entire course of their collaboration), it was obviously not going to be one of their emphatic successes. On this particular April morning the pair were in conference in Sullivan's flat on Queen Victoria Street to discuss the plans for a new piece. The atmosphere was a bit tense. Sullivan, possibly suffering from a slight attack of self-esteem as a result of his newly acquired knighthood, had written Gilbert a letter that was more or less in the nature of an ultimatum. He was tired, he said, of fairy tales and topsy-turvy situations, of potions and spells; he was tired of having to subordinate his music to the words. He wanted a story that would give him room to be a composer, where the music could speak for itself, a story of "human interest and probability," in which (and here he was particularly emphatic) the serious and comic scenes were to be kept apart, so that the music could let itself go, without having its sentimental passages punctured by wisecracks.

Gilbert had written a sharp answer, but, having thought things over, had agreed, in principle at least, to meet Sullivan's demands. He had a story that, he felt confident, would exactly fill the bill. It concerned a magic lozenge which, on being swallowed, immediately transformed the swallower into whatever person he or she was pretending to be. The sinner became a saint, the old hag became a flapper, et cetera, et cetera.

This was one of Gilbert's pet ideas, which he had broached before, and which was to obsess him until he finally embodied it, eight years later, in *The Mountebanks*. Sullivan had rejected it two years previously; he would have none of it now. The meeting ended with nothing settled.

Gilbert then, with rare generosity, suggested that Sullivan choose another librettist for his next operetta —as a matter of fact, for a time Sullivan did toy with the idea of setting a book and lyrics by Bret Harte.

Nothing came of that, however, and the pair met again. Once more Gilbert produced his "lozenge" plot—somewhat modified, but still a lozenge—and once more Sullivan refused to swallow it. Finally Gilbert announced, reluctantly but definitely, that he could not consent "to construct another plot for the next opera." The break looked like a permanent one.

At this juncture D'Oyly Carte, who had been slowly going mad, took a hand in the proceedings and finally effected a reconciliation. Gilbert withdrew his lozenge, and Sullivan, not to be outdone in politeness, agreed, sight unseen, to set whatever new, lozengeless libretto his partner might provide.

Just how he managed to reconcile the plot, when Gilbert finally produced it, with his demand for "a story of human interest and probability," history does not record. History does record the fact that he did. According to Gilbert, the idea of writing a Japanese operetta occurred to him one day when an ancient Japanese sword fell from the wall to the floor of his studio. Simultaneously his thoughts turned to a model Japanese village that had recently been erected at Knightsbridge, not far away. One thing led to another, the fruit of his labors finally emerging as the libretto of *The Mikado*.

He spent the second half of 1884 writing and rewriting the new story, which was badly needed. *Princess Ida* had been taken off, and the Savoy was being kept open by a revival of *Trial by Jury*. Sullivan, behind time as usual, did not get started on the music until just before Christmas, and had to deliver some of the music while rehearsals were going on. By working night and day he managed to finish the orchestration just a week before the opening.

Gilbert, who was always a relentless drillmaster at rehearsals, was particularly severe in preparing *The Mikado*. The comparative failure of *Princess Ida* still rankled, and he resolved to spare no pains in producing the new work. He spared none, including the cast and the chorus, reducing George Grossmith to such a state of nerves that he actually took to drugs.

The Mikado opened at the Savoy on the evening of

March 14, 1885, with the following cast:

The Mikado	R. Temple	*Pish-Tush*	Frederick Bovill
Nanki-Poo	Durward Lely	*Yum-Yum*	Leonora Braham
Ko-Ko	George Grossmith	*Pitti-Sing*	Jessie Bond
Pooh-Bah		*Peep-Bo*	Sybil Grey
	Rutland Barrington	*Katisha*	Rosina Brandram

(There was also the Mikado's umbrella carrier, a mute part that was not listed in the cast but that has always been included in subsequent productions. In August the authors introduced a new character, Mr. Go-To, originally sung by Rudolph Lewis, one of the chorus basses. Go-To has no lines, but takes the place of Pish-Tush in the madrigal when the actor playing the latter role finds the bass part too much for him.)

The new piece was an uproarious success from the start and ran close to two years. The story of its pirated production in New York is probably so familiar that there is no need here to do more than summarize it. Briefly, an American producer, one John C. Duff, procuring a piano score of the new operetta, had an orchestration made of it, rehearsed a company, and opened at the Union Square Theatre, on August 8, 1885. D'Oyly Carte, who had got wind of the piracy, secretly prepared and rehearsed a complete English *Mikado* company and as secretly embarked for New York. He and his company arrived on the eighteenth, and opened on the evening of Wednesday, the nineteenth, at the Fifth Avenue Theatre. D'Oyly Carte's production was so far superior that Duff was finally forced to take to the road. The variant to this tale, to the effect that Carte opened on the twentieth, beating Duff's opening by five days, seems to be more picturesque than true.

The Mikado was a success wherever it was produced. Within a few years it had entertained enthusiastic audiences all over America and Australia, in Amsterdam, and in Berlin. There were a few objectors. Queen Victoria, for example, thought that the plot was "rather silly" (fancy that!), and the Japanese Ambassador tried to have the original production stopped, on the ground that it held his country and his emperor up to ridicule. But *The Mikado* has weathered their disapproval. As you read these lines, it is undoubtedly being performed somewhere in the world, the masterpiece of its creators and the most popular operetta ever written.

THE STORY

ACT I

Several Japanese gentlemen are passing the time in attitudes queer and quaint in the courtyard of the Lord High Executioner's palace. They explain—IF YOU WANT TO KNOW WHO WE ARE—who they are. Suddenly, handsome young Nanki-Poo rushes in and inquires where he may find the charming Yum-Yum, ward of Ko-Ko the tailor. He claims to be A WAND'RING MINSTREL. He has long loved Yum-Yum. Having heard that Ko-Ko, to whom she was betrothed, is to be beheaded for the capital offense of flirting, Nanki-Poo has seized this splendid opportunity to renew his suit.

A group of nobles enter and BEHOLD THE LORD HIGH EXECUTIONER—who is none other than this same Ko-Ko, now reprieved. He reveals the set of curious chances by which he was taken from a county jail and raised to the exalted office of Lord High Executioner. A conscientious man, he explains I'VE GOT A LITTLE LIST—a document cataloguing the sort of victims any self-respecting executioner would concentrate upon. As he discusses with Pooh-Bah (who is Lord High Everything Else) the plans for the festivities to follow his marriage this very day, his delicious fiancée Yum-Yum and her two friends—THREE LITTLE MAIDS FROM SCHOOL in all—come in giggling with girlish glee.

At once recognizing Nanki-Poo as the handsome young second trombone who once played in the local band, they in-troduce him to Ko-Ko, to whom he apologizes for being in love with Yum-Yum. Ko-Ko assures him that he is not a bit angry—that he is, in fact, delighted to have his judgment endorsed by a competent authority.

At last, though, Nanki-Poo finds Yum-Yum alone and is rapturous on finding she doesn't love her guardian. He then makes a startling confession. He is actually the son of—His Majesty, the Mikado! He is disguised only because of a natural panic at the possibility that he may have to marry Katisha, an elderly lady of the court who misconstrued his customary affability into expressions of love—and who has claimed his hand and everything else. And under his father's laws he would have to marry her or die.

Since flirting is a capital offense, Nanki-Poo doesn't *really* make love to Yum-Yum. He just shows her how he would kiss her WERE YOU NOT TO KO-KO PLIGHTED.

Meanwhile a terrible thing has happened. A message has come from the Mikado saying that if someone isn't executed pretty soon the post of Lord High Executioner will be abolished and the city of Titipu reduced to the rank of a village. Ko-Ko, who doesn't want to kill *anything*, is in despair. But this vanishes when he comes upon Nanki-Poo, who is about to terminate his own existence because of his hopeless love. Ko-Ko conceives the brilliant and kindly plan of appeasing the Mikado by executing Nanki-Poo, who agrees—but only upon the condition that he will be allowed to marry Yum-Yum and live with her a month. Ko-Ko points out that he adores Yum-Yum with passion tender and could not yield her with a ready will, did he not adore himself with passion tenderer still. It is, in a word, a deal, and there is some limited rejoicing.

This ceases abruptly when Katisha stalks in, penetrates Nanki-Poo's disguise, and claims him for her own. Although she tries to tell everyone that he is really the son of the Mikado, no one pays any attention to her, since all are too excited by the fact that HE'S GOING TO MARRY YUM-YUM.

ACT II

In Ko-Ko's garden, maidens BRAID THE RAVEN HAIR, paint the pretty face, and dye the coral lip of Yum-Yum in preparation for her wedding. Yum-Yum wonders, in her artless Japanese way, why it is that she is so much more attractive than anyone else in the world and states frankly that THE MOON AND I are far from shy.

A few moments of tearful bliss, contemplating the fact that BRIGHTLY DAWNS OUR WEDDING DAY, are interrupted by Ko-Ko, who has just learned that the law requires Nanki-Poo's widow to be buried alive with him when he is executed. This takes something of the edge off Yum-Yum's ecstasy, as she feels that burial alive is rather a stuffy death.

HERE'S A HOW-DE-DO, in short, until Ko-Ko hits on the ingenious scheme of faking an affidavit of execution by grossly insulting Pooh-Bah (who happens to be Lord Chief Justice and Commissioner of Police) with a sizable bribe.

The Mikado enters. With some interference from Katisha, his daughter-in-law elect, he makes it clear that he expects obedience FROM EVERY KIND OF MAN. He describes his excellent system of justice, its basic principle being that MY OBJECT ALL SUBLIME is to make the punishment fit the crime. Ko-Ko gives His Majesty the fake certificate of Nanki-Poo's execution and in a play-by-play description of the nonexistent execution tells him exactly how THE CRIMINAL CRIED before his demise. But Katisha, who had discovered Nanki-Poo's disguise, reads the certificate and points out with horror that the Mikado's son has been executed.

The Mikado mentions that, while he is not a *bit* angry, the law requires his bestowing on Ko-Ko and all involved the punishment that fits the crime of killing the heir apparent. He is a little vague on what that is, but believes it involves something lingering, with boiling oil in it. Ko-Ko flees to Nanki-Poo for help, but Nanki-Poo, already married to Yum-Yum, says that the only way out is for Ko-Ko to win the heart and hand of Katisha, because with Katisha married off, existence for Nanki-Poo will be as welcome as THE FLOWERS THAT BLOOM IN THE SPRING.

Ko-Ko rises to the occasion. He melts the heart of the fierce and elderly lady by telling her the story of TIT-WILLOW, the little bird who died for love. Katisha is moved and delighted. As soon as she marries Ko-Ko, Nanki-Poo comes out of hiding and presents Yum-Yum to his father as his daughter-in-law elect.

The threatened cloud has passed away and "brightly shines the dawning day."

If You Want to Know Who We Are

In spirited tempo

CHORUS

If you want to know who we are,——

We are gen-tle-men of Ja - pan;—— On—

man - y a vase and jar,—— On—

man - y a screen and fan, _____

We fig-ure in live-ly paint: Our at-ti-tude's queer and

quaint, You're wrong if you think it ain't.__ Oh!

If you think we are work'd by

strings, _____

Like a Jap - a -nese mar-io - nette, _____

You ___ don't un - der - stand these things: _____

It is sim - ply Court et - i - quette. _____

cresc.

Per - haps you sup-pose this throng ___ Can't keep it up all day

A Wand'ring Minstrel

Lightly and gracefully

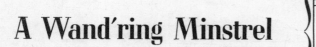

NANKI-POO

A wan-d'ring min-strel I,   A thing of shreds ___ and

legato

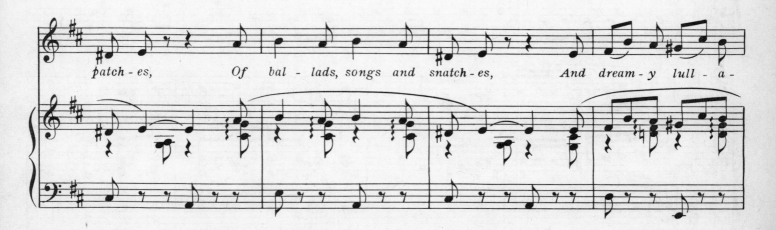

patch-es,   Of bal - lads, songs and snatch-es,   And dream-y lull - a-

by! _____ My cat-a-logue is long, Thro' ev - 'ry pas - sion

rang-ing, And to your hu-mours chang-ing I tune my sup-ple

song! _____ I tune my sup - - - ple

Slowly, with expression *p*

song! Are you in sen-ti-men-tal mood? I'll sigh with you,

Oh, _____ sor - row! On maid-en's cold-ness do you brood? I'll

do so, too, Oh,—— sor - row,—sor - 'row! I'll charm your will - ing

ears With songs of lov - ers' fears, While sym - pa - thet - ic tears— My cheeks be-

dew,—— Oh,—— sor - row,— sor - row!

March tempo

But if pa - tri - ot - ic sen - ti - ment is want - ed, I've

pa - tri - ot - ic bal - lads cut and dried; For wher- e'er our coun-try's ban-ner may be

plant-ed, All oth-er lo-cal ban-ners are de-fied! Our war-ri-ors, in ser-ried ranks as-

sem - bled, Nev-er quail, or they con-ceal it if they do, And I

should-n't be sur-pris'd if na-tions trem - bled Be-fore the might-y troops, the troops of Ti - ti -

Cheerfully, but not too fast

pu!

And if you call for a

song of the sea, We'll heave the cap-stan round, With a yeo heave - ho, for the

wind is _ free, Her an-chor's a-trip and her helm's a-lee, Hur-rah for the home-ward

MEN

bound! Yeo - ho _____ heave - ho, _____ Hur - rah for the home - ward

NANKI-POO

bound! To lay a-loft in a howl-ing breeze May tick-le a lands-man's

taste, But the hap-piest hour a _ sail - or _ sees Is when he's down At an

in - land town, With his Nan-cy on his knees, yeo - ho! And his arm _ a-round her

Behold the Lord High Executioner

Vigorous march tempo

ff

CHORUS of MEN

f

Be-hold the Lord High Ex - e - cu-tion-er! A

per - son-age of no-ble rank and ti - tle, A dig - ni - fied and po - tent

of - fi-cer, Whose func - tions are par-tic - u - lar - ly vi - tal! De-

fer, _____ de - fer, _____ To the Lord High Ex - e -

cu - tion - er! De - fer, _____ de - fer, _____ To the no - ble Lord, to the

no - ble Lord, to the Lord High _____ Ex - e - - cu - tion - er!

KO-KO

Tak - en from the coun - ty jail By a set of cur - ious

chan - ces; Lib - er - a - ted then on bail, On my own re - cog - ni -

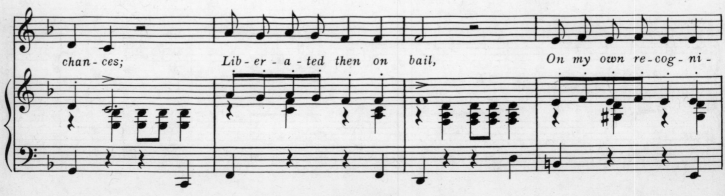

zan - ces; Waft-ed by a fav-'ring gale, As one some-times is in

tran-ces, To a height that few can scale, Save by long and wea-ry

dan-ces; Sure - ly, nev - er had a male, Un-der such like cir-cum-

stan-ces, So ad-ven - tur-ous a tale, Which may rank with most ro - man-ces.

Tak - en from the coun-ty jail By a set of cur-ious chan-ces;

Sure-ly, nev-er had a male, So ad-ven-tur-ous a tale. De-

fer, _____ de-fer, _____ To the Lord High Ex-e-cu-tion-er! De-

fer, _____ de-fer, _____ To the no-ble Lord, to the

no-ble Lord, to the Lord High Ex-e-cu-tion-er!

I've Got a Little List

Brightly and gracefully

mf

KO-KO

p *leggiero*

1. As some day it may hap-pen that a
(2. There's the) nig-ger ser-e-nad-er and the
(3. And that) Ni-si Pri-us nui-sance, who just

vic-tim must be found, I've got a lit-tle list, I've got a lit-tle list Of so-
oth-ers of his race, And the pia-no or-gan-ist, I've got him on the list! And the
now is rath-er rife, The Ju-di-cial hu-mor-ist, I've got him on the list! All

ci-e-ty of-fend-ers who might well be un-der-ground, And who
peo-ple who eat pep-per-mint and puff it in your face, They
fun-ny fel-lows, com-ic men and clowns of pri-vate life, They'd

never would be miss'd, who nev-er would be miss'd! There's the pes-ti-len-tial nui-san-ces who
nev-er would be miss'd, they nev-er would be miss'd! Then the i-di-ot who prais-es, with en-
none of 'em be miss'd, they'd none of 'em be miss'd! And a-pol-o-get-ic states-men of a

write for au-to-graphs, All peo-ple who have flab-by hands and
thu-si-as-tic tone, All cen-tur-ies but this and ev-'ry
com-pro-mis-ing kind, Such as What-d'ye-call-him, Thing-'em-bob, and

ir-ri-tat-ing laughs, All chil-dren who are up in dates, and
coun-try but his own; And the la-dy from the prov-in-ces, who
like-wise Nev-er-mind, And 'St-'st-'st and What's-his-name, and

floor you with 'em flat, All per-sons who in shak-ing hands shake
dress-es like a guy, And "who does-n't think she waltz-es, but would
al-so You-know-who, The task of fill-ing up the blanks I'd

hands with you like that, And all third per-sons who on spoil-ing tête-ā-têtes in-sist, They'd
rath-er like to try", And that sin-gu-lar a-nom-a-ly, the la-dy nov-el-ist, I
rath-er leave to you. But it real-ly does-n't mat-ter whom you put up-on the list, For they'd

CHORUS of MEN

none of 'em be miss'd, they'd none of 'em be miss'd! He's got 'em on the list, he's
don't think she'd be miss'd, I'm sure she'd not be miss'd! He's got her on the list, he's
none of 'em be miss'd, they'd none of 'em be miss'd! You may put 'em on the list, you may

got 'em on the list, And they'll none of 'em be miss'd, they'll
got her on the list, And I don't think she'll be miss'd, I'm
put 'em on the list, And they'll none of 'em be miss'd, they'll

1.-2.   KO-KO   3.

none of 'em be miss'd! 2. There's the
sure she'll not be miss'd! 3. And that
none of 'em be   miss'd!

[259]

Three Little Maids from School

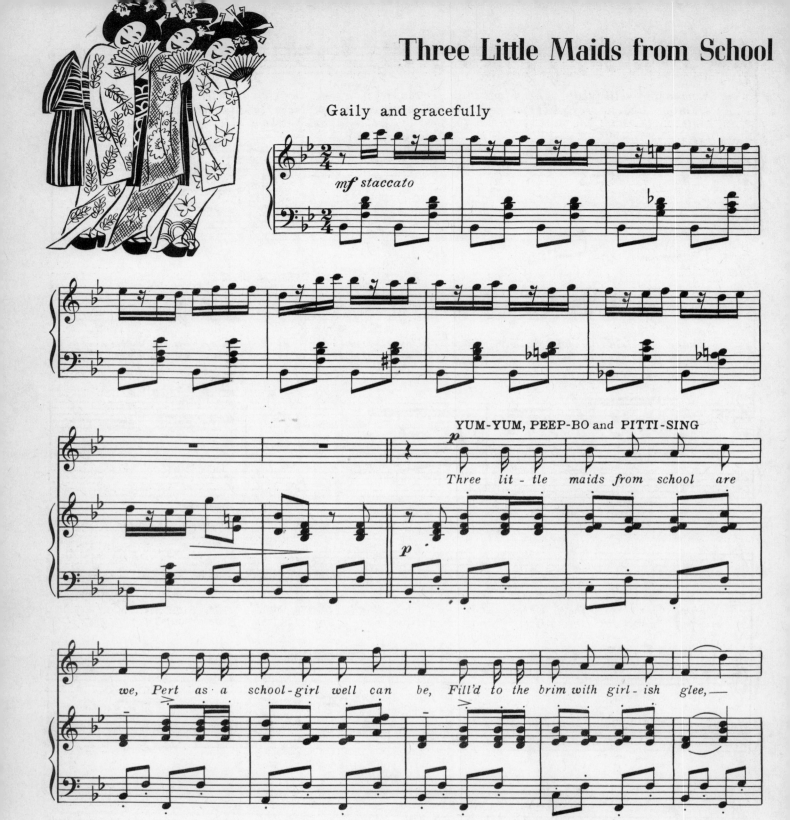

Gaily and gracefully

mf staccato

YUM-YUM, PEEP-BO and PITTI-SING

Three lit - tle maids from school are

we, Pert as a school-girl well can be, Fill'd to the brim with girl-ish glee,—

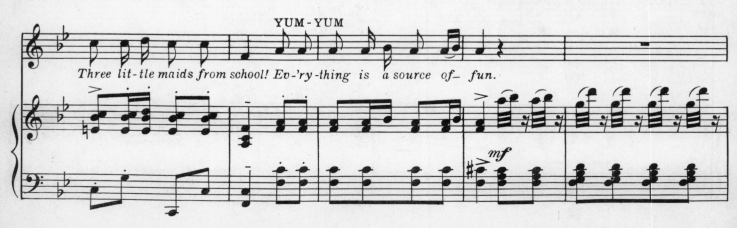

YUM-YUM

Three lit - tle maids from school! Ev-'ry-thing is a source of— fun.

PEEP-BO

No - bod - y's safe, for we care for_ none!

PITTI-SING

Life is a joke that's just be - gun!

ALL

Three lit - tle maids from school!

Three lit - tle maids who, all un - war - y, Come from a la - dies'

sem - i - nar - y, Freed from its gen - ius tu - te - lar - y,

Three lit - tle maids from school, Three lit - tle maids — from school!

YUM-YUM

One lit - tle maid is a bride, Yum-Yum,

PEEP-BO

Two lit - tle maids in at - ten - dance come,

PITTI-SING

Three lit - tle maids is the to - tal sum,

ALL

Three lit - tle maids from school!

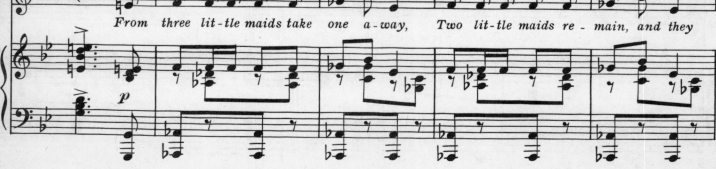

YUM-YUM

From three lit - tle maids take one a - way,

PEEP-BO

Two lit - tle maids re - main, and they

Were You Not to Ko-Ko Plighted

Slowly, with expression

NANKI-POO

Were you not to Ko-Ko plight-ed, I would say in ten-der tone, "Lov'd one, let us be u-

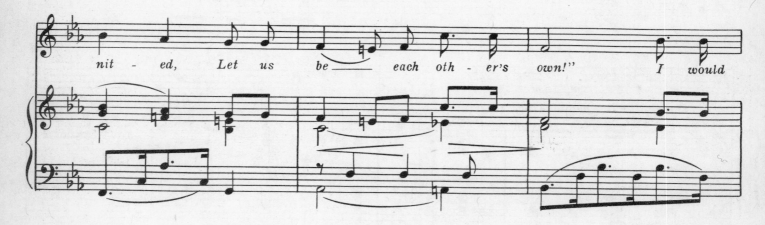

nit-ed, Let us be____ each oth-er's own!" I would

merge all rank and sta-tion, World-ly sneers are nought to

Slowly, with expression

ta - - tion, Such a theme I'll not dis - cuss, And on no con - sid - er-

espr.

rall.

a - tion Will I kiss you fond - ly thus, Will I kiss you fond - ly

rall.   *dim.*

Again fast

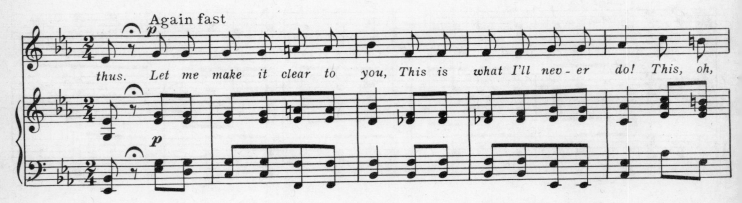

thus. Let me make it clear to you, This is what I'll nev - er do! This, oh,

p   *p*

this, oh, this oh, this, This ___ is what I'll

f   *f*

YUM-YUM

nev - er, ___ nev - er do! This, oh, this, oh,

mp   *mp*

this, oh, this, this, —— Is what I'll nev - er do! He'll

NANKI-POO *YUM-YUM*

nev - er do! I'll nev - er do! He'll nev - er do! Oh, this, This

NANKI-POO *YUM-YUM* *NANKI-POO* *BOTH*

Broad

is what {he'll / I'll} nev - er, nev - er do!

For He's Going to Marry Yum-Yum

Brightly

Gracefully

For — he's go-ing to mar-ry Yum - Yum! Yum-Yum! Your

an - ger pray bur - y, For all will be mer-ry, I think you had bet - ter suc-

CHORUS   PITTI-SING

cumb! Cumb-cumb! And join our ex-pres-sions of glee. On this

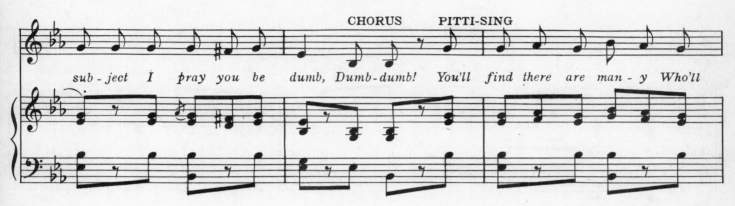

CHORUS   PITTI-SING

sub-ject I pray you be dumb, Dumb-dumb! You'll find there are man-y Who'll

CHORUS   PITTI-SING

wed for a pen-ny, The word for your guid-ance is "Mum," Mum-Mum! There's

PITTI-SING and CHORUS

lots of good fish in the sea! On this sub-ject we pray you be

dumb-dumb-dumb, We think you had bet-ter suc-cumb-cumb-cumb! You'll

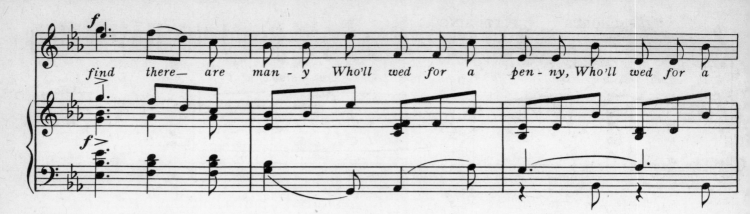

find there— are man-y Who'll wed for a pen-ny, Who'll wed for a

pen-ny, There are lots of— good fish in the sea! There are

lots of good fish in the sea! There's lots of good fish, good fish in the

sea! There's lots of good fish, good fish in the sea, in the sea, in the

sea, in the sea, in the sea!—

Braid the Raven Hair

grace Of her la - dy - ship! Art and

na - ture, thus al - lied, Go to make a

pret - ty bride! Art and na - ture, thus al - lied, Go to make a

pret - ty bride.

The Moon and I

Slowly with expression

p YUM-YUM

1. The sun, whose rays Are all a-blaze With ev-er - liv-ing glo-ry,
2. Ob-serve his flame, That plac-id dame, The moon's Ce - les-tial High-ness;

Does not de-ny His maj-es-ty He scorns to tell a sto-ry!
There's not a trace Up-on her face Of dif-fi-dence or shy-ness:

He don't ex-claim, "I blush for shame, So kind-ly be in-dul-gent."
She bor-rows light That, thro' the night, Man-kind may all ac-claim her!

But, fierce and bold, In fie - ry gold, He glo - ries all ef - ful - gent!
And, truth to tell, She lights up well, So I, for one, don't blame her!

I mean to rule the earth,
Ah, pray make no mis - take,

As he the sky, We real - ly know our worth, The sun and I!
We are not shy; We're ver - y wide a - wake, The moon and I!

I mean to rule the earth, As he the sky, We real - ly know our worth, The sun and
Ah, pray make no mis - take, We are not shy; We're ver - y wide a - wake, The moon and

I!
I!

Brightly Dawns Our Wedding Day

In lively spirited tempo

YUM-YUM

1. Bright-ly dawns our wed-ding day; Joy-ous
(2. Let us) dry the read-y tear, Though the

hour, we give thee greet-ing! Whith-er,— whith-er art thou fleet-ing? Fick-le
hours are sure-ly creep-ing Lit-tle— need for woe-ful weep-ing, Till the

mo-ment, pri-thee stay! Fick-le— mo-ment, pri-thee stay!
sad sun-down is near, Till the— sad sun-down is near.

gal, Sing a — mer-ry mad-ri - gal— Sing a— mer-ry mad-ri-

gal,— Fa la, Fa la, Fa————— la la la la, Fa—

— la la la la, Fa——— la la la la, Fa——— la la la la la la la, Fa

la la la, Fa— la, Fa la la la, Fa— la, Fa la la, Fa la

la, Fa la————— la. 2. Let us la.

Here's a How-De-Do

With exultant gaiety

f

YUM-YUM

mf

Here's a how-de-do! If I mar-ry you, When your time has come to per-ish, Then the maid-en whom you cher-ish Must be slaugh-ter'd too! Here's a how-de-do! Here's a how-de-do!

suit her no-tion, Bur-i-al it brings! Here's a state of things!

Here's a state of things! *mf* **ALL THREE** With a pas-sion that's in-

tense I wor-ship and— a - dore, But the laws of com-mon sense We ought-n't

to— ig - nore. If what he says is true, 'Tis death to mar-ry

you! Here's a pret-ty state of things! Here's a pret-ty how-de-do!

From Every Kind of Man

KATISHA

clar'd Par - tic - u - lar - ly cor - rect; But they're noth - ing at all, com -
light, My free - dom from all — de - fect, Is in - sig - nif - i - cant

par'd With those of his daugh - ter - in - law e - lect!
quite, Com - par'd with his daugh - ter - in - law e - lect!

Bow,

bow, To his daugh - ter - in - law e - lect!

f CHORUS

Bow,

bow, To his daugh - ter - in - law e - lect.

MIKADO

2. In a

My Object All Sublime

Very lively

MIKADO

ob - ject all sub - lime   I shall a - chieve in time,   To let the pun - ish - ment

fit the crime, The pun - ish - ment fit the crime;   And make each pris - 'ner pent   Un-

will - ing - ly re - pre - sent   A source of in - no - cent mer - ri - ment, Of   in - no - cent mer - ri - ment!

1. All
2. The

pros - y dull so - ci - e - ty sin - ners, Who chat - ter and bleat and bore,—— Are
ad - ver - tis - ing quack who wea - ries With tales of count - less cures,—— His

sent to hear ser - mons From mys - ti - cal Ger - mans Who preach from ten till
teeth, I've en - act - ed, Shall all be ex - tract - ed By ter - ri - fied am - a -

four. The am - a - teur ten - or, whose vo - cal vil - lain - ies
teurs. The mu - sic - hall sing - er at - tends a ser - ies Of

All de - sire—— to shirk, Shall, dur - ing off - hours, —— Ex -
mass - es and fugues and "ops" By Bach, in - ter - wov - en With

only suffer To ride on a buffer In Parliament'ry trains.} My
cloth untrue, With a twisted cue, And elliptical billiard balls!

object all sublime I shall achieve in time, To

let the punishment fit the crime, The punishment fit the crime; And

make each pris'ner pent Unwillingly represent A

source of innocent merriment, Of innocent merriment! -ment!—

The Criminal Cried

With ease and not too fast

Ko-Ko 1. The

crim-i-nal cried, as he dropp'd him down, In a state of wild a-
shiv-er'd and shook as he gave the sign For the stroke he did-n't de-
tho' you'd have said that head was dead (For its own-er dead was

leggiero

larm, With a fright-ful, fran-tic, fear-ful frown, I bar'd my big right
serve; When all of a sud-den his eye met mine, And it seem'd to brace his
he), It stood on its neck, with a smile well bred, And bow'd three times to

arm.__ I seiz'd him by his lit-tle pig-tail, And
nerve;__ For he nod-ded his head and kiss'd his hand, And he
me!__ It was none of your im-pu-dent off-hand nods, But as

[288]

on his knees fell he, As he squirm'd and strug-gled, And gur-gled and gug-gled, I
whis-tled an air,_ did he, As the sa-bre true Cut clean-ly through His
hum - ble as_ could be; For it clear-ly knew The def-er-ence due To a

drew my snick-er-snee,_____ my snick-er-snee!_ Oh,
cer - vi - cal ver-te-brae,_____ his ver-te-brae!_ When a
man of ped - i - gree,_____ of ped - i - gree!_ And it's

ne'er shall I For-get the cry, Or the shriek that shriek-ed he,___ As I
man's a-fraid, A beau-ti-ful maid Is a cheer-ing sight to see;___ And it's
oh, I vow, This death - ly bow Was a touch-ing sight to see;___ Though

gnash'd my teeth, When from_ its sheath I drew_ my snick-er-
oh,_ I'm glad That mo - ment sad Was sooth'd_ by sight of
trunk - less, yet It could-n't for - get The def - er - ence due to

[289]

CHORUS

snee! — We know him well, He can-not tell Un - true or ground-less
me! — Her ter - ri - ble tale You can't as-sail, With truth it quite a-
me! — This haugh - ty youth, He speaks the truth When - ev-er he finds it

tales; — He al - ways tries To ut - ter lies, And
grees; — Her taste ex - act For fault - less fact A-
pays; — And in this case, It all took place Ex -

1.-2.
ev - 'ry time he fails. — Pitti-Sing 2. He
mounts to a dis - ease. — Pooh-Bah 3. Now
act - ly as he

3.
says! Ex-act - ly, ex - act - ly, ex-act - ly, ex-

act - ly as he says! _____

The Flowers That Bloom in the Spring

In gay tempo

Nanki-Poo 1. The flow-ers that bloom in the spring, Tra-la, Breathe
Ko-Ko 2. The flow-ers that bloom in the spring, Tra-la, Have

molto leggiero

prom-ise of mer-ry sun-shine, As we mer-ri-ly dance and we
noth-ing to do with the case. I've got to take un-der my

sing, Tra-la, We wel-come the hope that they bring, Tra-la, Of a
wing, Tra-la, A most un-at-trac-tive old thing, Tra-la, With a

sum-mer of ros - es and wine, Of a sum-mer of ros - es and wine. And
car - i - ca-ture of a face, With a car - i - ca-ture of a face; And

that's what we mean when we say that a thing Is wel - come as flow - ers that
that's what I mean when I say or I sing: "Oh, both - er the flow - ers that

bloom in the spring. Tra - la - la-la-la, — Tra - la - la-la-la, — The
bloom in the spring." Tra - la - la-la-la, — Tra - la - la-la-la, — "Oh,

flow - ers that bloom in the spring. Tra - la - la-la-la, — Tra -
both - er the flow - ers of spring!" Tra - la - la-la-la, — Tra -

la - la-la-la, — Tra - la-la-la-la - la.
la - la-la-la, — Tra - la-la-la-la - la. —

Tit-Willow

Slowly and with warmth

mp

p KO-KO

1. On a   tree by a riv - er a   lit - tle tom - tit   Sang___
(2. He)   slapp'd at his chest, as he   sat on that bough,   Sing-ing
(3. Now I)   feel just as sure as I'm   sure that my name   Is - n't

p

"Wil - low, tit - wil - low, tit - wil - low "   And I   said to him, "Dick - y - bird,
"Wil - low, tit - wil - low, tit - wil - low!"   And a   cold per - spi - ra - tion be -
Wil - low, tit - wil - low, tit - wil - low,   That 'twas blight - ed af - fec - tion that

why do you sit   Sing - ing   'Wil - low,   tit - wil - low, tit -
span - gled his brow,   Oh,   wil - low,   tit - wil - low, tit -
made him ex - claim,   "Oh,   wil - low,   tit - wil - low, tit -

RUDDIGORE
OR
The Witch's Curse

RUDDIGORE

OR
The Witch's Curse

HE success of *The Mikado* (it ran for a total of 672 performances) had opposite effects upon the two partners. It started Gilbert making plans for a new opera and created in Sullivan an immense desire not to work. As a matter of fact, a family misfortune kept him from working for a time. His brother Fred's widow had remarried and moved to California. She died early in 1885, and Sullivan went to America in the summer of that year to look after her children. Upon his arrival he found himself a national figure (even if the producers of his works didn't pay him royalties) and was hounded by reporters all the way from New York to Los Angeles. He took the children (one of them his adopted son) to the Yosemite Valley, then came back by easy stages to New York, where he saw a performance of *The Mikado* and made a speech suggesting that Americans give the man who invented a song or a poem the same legal protection as the man who invented a new beer tap. Then to Philadelphia, to help Carte put on *The Mikado* production there, and then, in October, back to London.

Gilbert was waiting for him, hoping that he would consider "the (as it seems to me) admirable plot I proposed to you last year"—in other words, the dear old lozenge. Sullivan, regretful but firm, would have none of it, so Gilbert, baffled, returned once more into the silences. He was knocking on his partner's door again in a January blizzard, to read him a new story. This time, Sullivan was delighted, and together they mapped out the complete plot. But, he warned Gilbert, he couldn't begin the music at once. First, he must compose a new cantata that he had promised for the Leeds Festival in the fall. Since *The Mikado* was still playing to crowded houses, Gilbert had no objections.

The libretto of the cantata was a dramatization of Longfellow's *The Golden Legend*, for which he had paid Joseph Bennett five hundred pounds. He started the music early in the year, but the remoteness of the performance date (October) was too much for him.

Sullivan must have had newspaperman's blood in his veins; he never could work well except to an imminent deadline. Give him plenty of time, and his creative faculties were paralyzed. The spring went by, and nothing was done. June came, and still he had written little or nothing. Not until July did he get seriously to work—and then it was a matter of working night and day. To compose a cantata lasting over an hour, and orchestrate it in time to have the parts extracted and the chorus, soloists, and orchestra rehearsed—to do this in three months is no small feat.

He accomplished it, however, and *The Golden Legend*, performed on October 15, 1886, was greeted with frantic enthusiasm. Oddly enough, it was Sullivan who realized that he was tending more and more to lean toward the theater instead of the concert platform, even in his serious music. He is quoted as saying to the composer, Alexander Mackenzie, "I can't get away from it. When I was writing *The Legend*, and Elsie sang, at the most serious point of the story, 'I come here not to argue, but to die,' I quite regretted the chance of letting the chorus respond, after the approved Savoy fashion, 'Why, she doesn't come here to argue, but to die.'"

Gilbert promptly wrote to congratulate him on "what appears from all accounts to be the biggest thing you've done," and to remind him that the music for the new Savoy piece was not yet done. Now that the time was growing appropriately short (it was the end of October, and *The Mikado*'s successor was scheduled for production in January) Sullivan went to work in earnest on the score.

It is curious that two men who worked together for so many years should always have been, in a sense, strangers. Even in their work, they generally offered suggestions or criticisms through the medium of a third person. Sullivan told one mutual friend of theirs that although the new piece was supposed to be an opera, it was really "becoming a play with a few songs and some concerted music," and suggested that he hint to Gilbert that the music was being relegated to the background. Gilbert, on the contrary, told this same friend that though he liked the music, he felt that there was so much of it that the audience might lose the thread of the story, and that it might be a good idea to cut a couple of the numbers. This criticism seems a bit quaint, coming as it did from the man who had written the lyrics that were responsible for the "too much" music. If there were too many numbers, why had he written so many?

The new work was produced at the Savoy, under the name of *Ruddygore; or, The Witch's Curse*, "a new and original supernatural opera," on the evening of January 22, 1887. The cast was as follows:

MORTALS

Robin Oakapple	*Rose Maybud*
George Grossmith	Leonora Braham
Richard Dauntless	*Mad Margaret*......Jessie Bond
Durward Lely	*Dame Hannah*
Sir Despard Murgatroyd	Rosina Brandram
Rutland Barrington	*Zorah*........Josephine Findlay
Adam Goodheart	*Ruth*................Miss Lindsay
Rudolph Lewis	

GHOSTS

Sir Rupert Murgatroyd	*Sir Desmond Murgatroyd*
Mr. Price	Mr. Tuer
Sir Joseph Murgatroyd	*Sir Gilbert Murgatroyd*
Mr. Charles	Mr. Wilbraham
Sir Lionel Murgatroyd	*Sir Mervyn Murgatroyd* }
Mr. Trevor	*Sir Roderic Murgatroyd* }
Sir Conrad Murgatroyd	Mr. Cox
Mr. Burbank	

Ruddigore (as it is spelled now) got off to a bad start. It went well enough, on opening night, until the last twenty minutes or so, when the audience began to be restless. There was applause at the fall of the curtain, but there was also some faint but unmistakable booing from the gallery—the first that had ever greeted a Gilbert and Sullivan opera. The authors made some cuts after the opening and wrote a new last-act finale, but the impression of excessive length still lasted in the minds of the critics. Then, during the first weeks of the run, Grossmith was stricken with peritonitis and had to undergo an operation. Henry Lytton was rushed in to take his place. Lytton subsequently became a great favorite and was eventually famous as the last of the original Savoyards; but the haste with which he had to rehearse showed in his first performances of the part.

Then, too, the name gave offense. Some bright observer discovered that "ruddy" was very close to that completely taboo (to an Englishman) word, "bl—dy." The press commented upon it in horrified accents, and many people, believe it or not, were deterred from at-

tending the performance because of it. Gilbert changed the offending syllable by substituting an "i" for the "y"; even so, many of the "nice" people stayed away. The title is responsible, by the way, for one of the best of the Gilbert anecdotes. There are two versions, the most probable being, I think, the one favored by Hesketh Pearson. According to him, a friend of Gilbert's, meeting him on the street, said, "How's *Bloodygore* going?"

"You mean, *Ruddigore*," said Gilbert.

"Same thing," remarked the friend.

"Indeed?" observed Gilbert, icily. "Then if I say that I admire your ruddy countenance—which I do— it means that I like your bloody cheek—which I don't."

In his disgust, Gilbert suggested that the piece be called, *Kensington Gore; or, Not so Good as the Mikado*. But nobody laughed.

Then, to add to the tribulations of the authors, one of the songs—Richard Dauntless' opening ballad in the first act—nearly caused an international incident. The second verse will give you an idea of the language and sentiments of the number:

> Then our Captain he up and he says, says he,
> "That chap we need not fear—
>   We can take her, if we like,
>   She is sartin for to strike,
> For she's only a darned Mounseer,
>   D'ye see?
> She's only a darned Mounseer!
> But to fight a French fal-lal—it's like hittin' of a gal—
>   It's a lubberly thing for to do;
>   For we, with our faults,
>   Why, we're sturdy British salts,
> While she's only a Parley-voo,
>   D'ye see?
> While she's only a Parley-voo!"

The London correspondent of the Paris *Figaro* picked this up and wrote furiously in his paper of this insult to the French navy. On the other hand, certain British listeners saw fit to find the song an insult to the *British* navy. The net result of the controversy was a joint letter which Gilbert and Sullivan addressed to the editor of *Figaro*, in which they protested that it was far from their intention to ridicule a nation "as brave as it is chivalrous," and that their "only a Parley-voo" had "précisément autant de sens que 'rosbif' et 'goddam' employés pour ridiculer les anglais dans une comédie-burlesque française." This pacified the editor of *Figaro*, and England and France didn't go to war.

Nevertheless, the "witch's curse" seemed to lie heavy on *Ruddigore*. It ran for 288 performances—longer than *The Sorcerer* or *Princess Ida*; Gilbert, the one who, of the three partners, profited the least (Sullivan had his sheet-music royalties, and Carte had nothing at stake except his share of the investment), made thirty-five thousand dollars out of it. Nevertheless, it labored for years under the onus of being a flat failure, which it was not. It contains some of Gilbert's best writing and lyrics, and a good deal of Sullivan's best music, and is, altogether, a grand show. Its restoration to public favor is to the credit of an American organization, the Hinshaw Opera Company, which revived it in New York in 1920. It was introduced as one feature of a Gilbert and Sullivan season and turned out to be the hit of the entire series.

THE STORY

ACT I

The professional bridesmaids of the fishing village of Rederring, whose daily hours are from ten to four, are serenading lovely Rose Maybud. This is because she is the fairest maiden in the vicinity and, as such, is expected to require their services as soon as a youth is found bold enough to ask her hand in marriage.

Rose's Aunt Hannah tells the bridesmaids that she would gladly get married herself, to give them employment, were she not vowed to maidenhood. In her youth she loved Sir Roderic Murgatroyd, direct descendant of the very Sir Rupert Murgatroyd whose leisure and riches were usually employed in persecuting witches—until one witch, resenting this trait, placed a curse on his family, which required each lord of Ruddigore to commit a crime a day or die in agony. Sir Roderic, beloved of Hannah, finally rebelled—and died.

Sweet Rose Maybud enters with a book of etiquette, which is her Bible, and admits that IF SOMEBODY THERE CHANCED TO BE who loved her in a manner true, she would be happy to wed.

As soon as Aunt Hannah leaves, Robin Oakapple appears. He is a shy young farmer who loves Rose. Being too modest to make love to her in the first person, he tells her I KNOW A YOUTH who loves a little maid, and they pour out their hearts indulging only in third personalities. As Rose leaves, Old Adam enters and recognizes Robin as Sir Ruthven Murgatroyd in disguise. Robin admits that he fled his home to escape succeeding to the baronetcy, which would force him to commit a daily crime, and that his younger brother Despard, thinking him dead, is at the moment enjoying the title and suffering the curse.

Robin's half brother, a sailor unafflicted by diffidence, enters and hears from Robin that MY BOY, YOU MAY TAKE IT FROM ME, modesty doesn't pay. He promises to woo Rose in his brother's behalf, but when the time comes he woos her for himself instead, and Rose accepts him. However, she is so touched by the sportsmanlike way in which Robin accepts the shattering blow that she transfers her hand and heart to him. She can well afford to pity Mad Margaret, who loved Sir Despard Murgatroyd and was deserted by him as one of his daily crimes.

Sir Despard and a troupe of fashionable young bucks, tired of sophisticated pleasures, arrive in the village just in time for Rose's wedding. Disappointed Richard, who makes a practice of following the dictates of his heart, tells Sir Despard that Robin is actually his older brother, supposed to be dead. Sir Despard stops the wedding just in time by announcing the truth. Rose offers to marry him, but Despard, now free of the witch's curse, obeys the call of duty and takes Mad Margaret instead. Robin sadly accepts the title and the obligation of committing a daily crime.

ACT II

As, in the picture gallery of Ruddigore Castle, Robin and faithful Adam stare gloomily at the portraits of all the becursed Murgatroyds from the time of James I to the lately deceased Sir Roderic, Richard comes in to ask Robin's consent to marry Rose Maybud. Robin is about to commit his daily crime by imprisoning Rose, when Richard unfurls above her the Union Jack, which not even a wicked baronet may defy. So Robin gives his consent.

As soon as Robin is alone, the ancestors come out of their picture frames and Sir Roderic tells him how they enjoy themselves WHEN THE NIGHT WIND HOWLS. They scold Robin for committing inferior crimes such as forging his own will and making false income-tax returns ("Everybody does that," they point out). And they force him, by making him writhe in agony, to promise that he will do something a little more imaginative—abduct a lady, for example. The ex-Sir Despard enters with Mad Margaret, whom he has married, and Robin is so touched by their marital bliss that he decides to defy his ancestors at the risk of death. Meanwhile, Adam drags in the lady he has kidnaped and who turns out to be Rose's Aunt Hannah. She goes at Robin with a dagger and he calls on his ancestors to protect him. Sir Roderic obligingly leaves his frame and is filled with emotion on seeing Hannah, whom he loved while he lived. She tells him that this abduction is an outrage, that she never gave Robin encouragement. She reviews her years of faithful love for Roderic, resorting to poetic fancy with THERE GREW A LITTLE FLOWER.

Then Robin has a wonderful idea. Since, he says, "A Baronet of Ruddigore can only die through refusing to commit his daily crime. Therefore, to refuse to commit a daily crime is tantamount to suicide! But suicide is, itself, a crime—and so, by your own showing, you ought never to have died at all!" Sir Roderic agrees that this is excellent logic, immediately comes alive again, and embraces Hannah. Rose finally gives her heart to Robin (who has also theoretically committed suicide), and Richard finds happiness with one of the professional bridesmaids.

If Somebody There Chanced to Be

Moderate Waltz tempo

ROSE

1. If some-bod-y there chanced to be Who loved me in a man - ner true, My heart would point him out to me, And I would point him out to you.

2. If an - y well-bred youth I knew, Po - lite and gen - tle, neat and trim, Then I would hint as much to you, And you 'could hint as much to him.

(Referring to book of Etiquette)

But here____ it____

But here____ it____

[300]

I Know a Youth

(Hey, but she sick-ens as the days go by!). She can-not tell him all the
(Hey, but she sick-ens as the days go by!). Dai - ly she goes for to

sad,— sad— truth (Hey, but I think that lit-tle maid will die!).
weep— for to wail (Hey, but I think that lit-tle maid will die!).

ROBIN
Poor lit-tle man! Poor lit-tle maid! Poor lit-tle man!
Poor lit-tle maid! Poor lit-tle man! Poor lit-tle maid!

ROSE BOTH
Poor lit-tle maid!
Poor lit-tle man! Now tell me pray, and tell me true,

What in the world___ should the {maid-en / young man} do?

real - ly do be - lieve that tim - id youth will_ die!). *mp* **ROSE** Poor lit - tle man!

ROBIN Poor lit - tle maid! **ROSE** Poor lit - tle man! **ROBIN** Poor lit - tle maid!

BOTH I thank you, {sir,/miss,} for your coun-sel true; I'll tell that {maid_/youth_}

_ what {she/he} ought to do!

My Boy, You May Take It from Me

Fast and vivaciously

ROBIN

1. My boy, you may take it from me, That of all the af-flic-tions ac-
2. Now take, for ex-am-ple, my case: I've a bright in-tel-lec-tu-al
3. As a po-et, I'm ten-der and quaint, I've pas-sion and fer-vour and

curst With which a man's sad-dled And ham-pered and ad-dled, A
brain, In all Lon-don cit-y There's no one so wit-ty, I've
grace, From Ov-id and Hor-ace To Swin-burne and Mor-ris, They

dif-fi-dent na-ture's the worst. Though clev-er as clev-er can be, A
thought so a-gain and a-gain. I've a high-ly in-tel-li-gent face, My
all of them take a back place. Then I sing and I play and I paint: Though

Crich-ton of ear - ly ro - mance,
fea-tures can-not be de - nied,
none are ac - com-plished as I,

You must stir it and stump it, And
But, what - ev - er I try, sir, I
To say so were trea - son: You

blow your own trum-pet, Or, trust me, you have-n't a chance!
fail in and why, sir? I'm mod-es - ty per-son-i - fied!
ask me the reas - on? I'm dif - fi-dent, mod-est, and shy!

If you

wish in the world to ad - vance, Your mer-its you're bound to en - hance, You must stir it and stump it, And

blow your own trum-pet, Or, trust me; you have-n't a chance!

chance!

When the Night Wind Howls

There Grew a Little Flower

Slowly, with sentiment

HANNAH

1. There
(2. When she)
(3. Said)

1. grew a lit-tle flow-er 'Neath a great oak tree: When the
2. found that he was fick-le, Was that great oak tree, She was
3. she, "He loved me nev-er, Did that great oak tree, But I'm

1. tem-pest 'gan to low-er Lit-tle heed-ed she: No
2. in a pret-ty pick-le, As she well might be, But his
3. neith-er rich nor clev-er, And so why should he? But though

1. need had she to cow-er, For she dread-ed not its pow-er, She was
2. gal-lan-tries were mick-le, For death fol-lowed with his sick-le, And her
3. fate our for-tunes sev-er, To be con-stant I'll en-deav-our, Aye, for-

hap - py in the bow - er Of her great oak tree!
tears be - gan to trick - le For her great oak tree! } Sing hey, Lack-a-
ev - er and for - ev - er, To my great oak tree!

day! _____ Sing _ hey, Lack-a-day Let the

tears fall free For the pret-ty lit-tle flow'r and the great oak tree! Sing

hey, Lack-a - day! _ Sing hey, Lack-a - day! _ Sing

Sir Roderic

Sing hey, _____ Lack-a-day! Sing hey, _____ Lack-a-day!

hey, lack-a-day! Let the tears fall free, For the pret-ty lit-tle flow-er and the

Hey, lack-a-day! Let the tears fall free, For the pret-ty lit-tle flow-er and the

tenderly

rit. |1.-2. *a tempo*

great oak tree!

great oak tree!

2. When she
3. Said

rit. *a tempo*

|3.

tree! Sing hey, Lack-a-day!

tree! Sing hey, Lack-a-day!

pp rit.

Hey, lack-a-day, lack-a-day, lack-a-day!

Hey, lack-a-day, lack-a-day, lack-a-day!

dim. *pp rit.* *morendo*

ppp

THE YEOMEN OF THE GUARD

OR

The Merryman and His Maid

THE YEOMEN OF THE GUARD

OR

The Merryman and His Maid

SULLIVAN'S health was growing steadily worse. He had still twelve years to live, but they were never to be entirely free from discomfort and pain. *Ruddigore* safely launched, he went to Monte Carlo, hoping to find the sun, but encountered an earthquake instead. Then to Naples, where an unusually bad attack prostrated him for a time. He recovered in time to go to Berlin to conduct a special performance of *The Golden Legend* in honor of the ninetieth birthday of the old Kaiser Wilhelm I, on March 26, 1887. It was not an auspicious occasion, chiefly because of the fact that the principal soloist, one Madame Pattini, had neither voice nor musicianship. His insistence on an all-British orchestra had not endeared him to the critics in the first place, and they seized the opportunity to haul him and his music over the coals. However, he obtained permission to conduct a second performance, and telegraphed to Emma Albani, who was in Antwerp. She came to the rescue, sang magnificently, and turned the second hearing into a triumph.

Back in London, Gilbert came forward with an idea for a new piece, which turned out to be our old friend, George W. Lozenge! Once more Sullivan flatly refused to consider it, but then weakened sufficiently to agree to consider it if Gilbert would revise it. This Gilbert agreed to do. In the meantime, Sullivan busied himself with setting an *Ode* by Tennyson for which the Prince of Wales had asked him to do the music—"busied," that is, in the usual Sullivanesque fashion, which meant toying with it for several weeks and then writing the whole thing in four hours.

Four months after their first meeting Gilbert was back again with his lozenge; and this time Sullivan struck. No lozenge, in any shape or form. Gilbert struck, too, announcing that he had no intention of thinking up another libretto, and that Sullivan could set this one or none at all. For a time it looked as if the breach between the two would be permanent. Meanwhile, *Ruddigore* closed, on November 5, 1887, with

nothing new to follow it. Carte kept the Savoy open with a series of revivals, the first of which, *Pinafore*, on November 12, was the occasion of a reconciliation between the authors. Sullivan, conducting an orchestral rehearsal, saw Gilbert, who confided that he had a brand-new plot, with not even a shadow of a lozenge in it. Waiting for a train at the Uxbridge railway station, he had noticed a poster of the Tower Furnishing Company which displayed a picture of one of the Beefeaters of the Tower of London, and had instantly conceived the idea for a new opera. It was to be called *The Tower of London*, or perhaps *The Tower Warden* —no, possibly *The Beefeater*. At all events, it wasn't going to be *The Lozenge*, and as the story struck Sullivan as possessing just the human and dramatic qualities that he had been looking for, he agreed to set it.

So saying, he went for a trip to Algiers, and then to southern France. It was from Monte Carlo that he wrote to Gilbert to say that he was through with comic opera. The constant exhortations of his high-brow friends, to stop writing trivia and do Big Things, were beginning to take effect. Furthermore, he seemed particularly irked by the fact that a comic opera by Alfred Cellier, *Dorothy*, was approaching its five hundredth performance. If Sir Arthur Sullivan, England's knight of music, was going to have to compete for popularity with a commoner, why go on?

Gilbert, who was already at work on the libretto, handled him with considerable skill, pointing out that "we have the best theatre, the best company, the best composer, and (though I say it) the best librettist in England working together—we are world known and as much an institution as Westminster Abbey—and to scatter this splendid organization because *Dorothy* has run 500 nights is, to my way of thinking, to give up a gold mine. What is *Dorothy*'s success to us? It is not even the same class of piece as ours. Is no piece but ours to run 500 or 600 nights? Did other companies dissolve because *Mikado* ran 650 nights?" He concluded by giving Sullivan a tip on a system for playing roulette, which is probably what turned the trick.

The *Pinafore* revival had been succeeded by *The Pirates of Penzance* on March 17; this, in turn, was succeeded by *The Mikado*, on June 8. Incidentally, the closing of the series, late in September, marked the resignation of Rutland Barrington, who had been with Gilbert and Sullivan since the days of *The Sorcerer*. There was no part for him in the new piece (Gilbert probably knew of his decision to leave the company), and besides, he wanted to become an actor-manager in his own right. He asked Gilbert to write him a play, and the latter obliged with *Brantinghame Hall*, a mixture of satire and melodrama that has been described as probably the worst play ever written—or, at least, produced. It was a prompt failure, and even Gilbert's generous refusal to accept the royalties due him did not prevent poor Barrington's going into bankruptcy.

Meanwhile Sullivan had conducted a performance of *The Golden Legend* in London, in May, at which occasion Queen Victoria was present and told Sullivan that he ought to write a grand opera. "You would do it so well," she said.

He probably agreed with her, but nevertheless started work on the new Savoy piece in July. As usual, he got little or nothing done until about five weeks before the scheduled opening, when he went to work in earnest, writing part of the daytime and all night. Gilbert, having embarked on a libretto that totally lacked his usual topsy-turvy brand of comedy, seems to have been seized with qualms. He worried about the seriousness of the story and kept pointing out to Sullivan that it took a long time getting under way—meaning, getting to the comic scenes. One of his particular worries was the opening, with just one person on the stage. It was his own idea, but he was the first to be skeptical about it. About a week before the opening he gave the piece its fourth and ultimate title. Accordingly, *The Yeomen of the Guard; or, The Merryman and His Maid*, opened at the Savoy on Wednesday evening, October 3, 1888.

This was the cast:

Jack Point George Grossmith	*Second Yeoman* Mr. Metcalf
Sergeant Meryll	*Third Yeoman* Mr. Merton
Richard Temple	*Fourth Yeoman*
Sir Richard Cholmondeley	Rudolph Lewis
W. Brownlow	*First Citizen* Mr. Redmond
Colonel Fairfax	*Second Citizen* Mr. Boyd
Courtice Pounds	*Elsie Maynard*
Leonard Meryll W.R.Shirley	Geraldine Ulmar
Wilfred Shadbolt	*Phoebe Meryll* Jessie Bond
W. H. Denny	*Dame Carruthers*
The Headsman Mr. Richards	Rosina Brandram
First Yeoman Mr. Wilbraham	*Kate* Rose Hervey

Gilbert was beside himself with nervousness on the opening night, driving Jessie Bond nearly mad by coming on the stage time and again, as she sat at her spinning wheel ready for her opening number, to make sure that everything was "all right." He always was nervous at openings, worrying the company to death with last-minute warnings and reminders and leaving the theater the minute the curtain rose, not to return until it was time to take his curtain call. "What I suffered during those hours, no man can tell. I have spent them at the club; I once went to a theatre alone, to see a play; I have walked up and down the street; but no matter where I was, agony and apprehension possessed me." With one exception, according to Hesketh Pearson, he never saw an actual performance of one of the Savoy operas. It was Sullivan, the semi-invalid, who strode into the orchestra pit, cool and collected, and conducted the performance without a tremor.

The opening-night reception of *The Yeomen* was riotous, and papers were enthusiastic—so much so that the authors thought they had another *Mikado* to their credit. But though it had a respectable run, it was not one of their great successes. Both Gilbert and Sullivan considered it their best work. Sullivan was especially fond of the overture, which he thought could well be played on a symphonic program. But if public opinion insisted upon rating *The Yeomen* below *Pinafore*, *The Pirates*, and *The Mikado*, public opinion had a good deal of right on its side. The trouble with the book of *The Yeomen* is that it is a grand-opera story, but not grand enough; some of the lyrics, delightful as they are, sound out of mood with the plot. The score suffers from the same defect. It is serious in intent, but not weighty enough to carry the story. Altogether, the piece is a grand opera written in terms of operetta. None of which prevents many of the numbers, taken by themselves, from being among the best that Gilbert and Sullivan ever wrote.

THE STORY

ACT I

One fine day in the year fifteen-something, Phoebe Meryll is spinning on the Tower Green and meditating upon the difficulties that arise WHEN MAIDEN LOVES. Phoebe is constantly engaged in repulsing the crude advances of Wilfred, Head Jailor and Assistant Tormentor of the Tower of London. Wilfred pleads that he didn't become an Assistant Tormentor because he liked assistant tormenting; but this does no good, because Phoebe is really in love with Colonel Fairfax, the bravest, the handsomest, and the best young man in England. Unfortunately, Colonel Fairfax's eligibility is handicapped by the fact that he is doomed to be beheaded on the Tower Green within an hour for alleged dealings with the Devil.

Not unnaturally, Phoebe hates the Tower and its sanguine history, but Dame Carruthers, the Tower Housekeeper, reminds her of its origin WHEN OUR GALLANT NORMAN FOES took over.

Colonel Fairfax enters under guard and philosophically wonders, as befits a man who has only an hour of it left, IS LIFE A BOON? He explains to the Lieutenant that he was charged with sorcery by a jealous cousin who will inherit his estate if he, Fairfax, dies unmarried. Being a chivalrous gentleman, he therefore begs the Lieutenant to marry him to the poorest woman that he can find, so that she may inherit the Fairfax name—to say nothing of a hundred crowns.

Just then, Jack Point, a strolling jester, enters with his companion, a pretty strolling singer named Elsie Maynard. Egged on by the citizenry, they entertain with a song: I HAVE A SONG TO SING, O! The Lieutenant rescues them from the mob, promptly makes Jack Point his official jester, and selects Elsie as an ideal wife for Colonel Fairfax. Point permits his betrothed to do this, making it quite clear that—

> Though as a general rule of life
> I don't allow my promised wife,
> My lovely bride that is to be,
> To marry anyone but me,
> Yet if the fee is promptly paid,
> And he, in well-earned grave,
> Within the hour is duly laid,
> Objection I will waive!

The Lieutenant blindfolds Elsie and marries her to Fairfax. Phoebe meanwhile steals the Tower keys by pilfering them from Wilfred, deceitfully telling him how happy she would be WERE I THY BRIDE. She then gives the keys to her father, who helps Fairfax to escape by disguising him as a Yeoman of the Guard, in a uniform borrowed from Phoebe's brother, Leonard Meryll. Since Leonard is unknown in London, Sergeant Meryll introduces Fairfax as his son to all assembled, the real Leonard being meanwhile in hiding. Wilfred seizes this opportunity to tell Fairfax that to his fraternal care he entrusts Phoebe. Fairfax takes advantage of this pleasant situation by exchanging a few dozen brotherly kisses with Phoebe.

When the moment for the execution comes, the Tower guards are horrified to discover that their prisoner has escaped. Poor Jack Point mourns that Elsie, whom he loves, is saddled with a husband, while Elsie, who had counted on widowhood and a hundred crowns rather than wifehood,

faints in the arms of Fairfax. She has fallen deeply in love with Fairfax, but of course believes that he is Leonard Meryll and does not realize that he is her husband.

ACT II

Jack Point, jilted by Elsie, broods in the moonlight, reading up on bad old jokes, when Wilfred tells him how easy he thinks it is to be a good jester. Point sings, OH, A PRIVATE BUFFOON is a lighthearted loon—but shows him his error. He then agrees to teach Wilfred all his original songs, riddles, and paradoxes in return for a perjured statement that Fairfax is dead.

Fairfax himself, unaware of his bride's identity, is upset by the idea that, although he is free both in life and limb, he is bound to an unknown bride. Dame Carruthers, thinking that Fairfax is Leonard, informs him that Elsie loves him, but adds that through certain delirious ravings of Elsie's, she believes that the poor child is married to Fairfax. They muse upon this STRANGE ADVENTURE. Then Colonel Fairfax, delighted that it is the lovely Elsie to whom he is wed, tests her fidelity by wooing her in the guise of Leonard. Her fidelity proves high test.

Suddenly they hear a shot. Wilfred rushes in with Jack Point and declares—as per contract—that while Fairfax was attempting to escape he dispatched him through the head with an ounce or two of lead.

But now, when Point begs Elsie to marry him, the disguised Fairfax tells him that A MAN WHO WOULD WOO A FAIR MAID must have more to offer than a jester's bag of tricks. And, to the despair of the self-sacrificing Phoebe, who helped arrange his disguise, he continues his pursuit of Elsie as together they contemplate the joy that ensues WHEN A WOOER GOES A-WOOING.

In her disappointment, Phoebe lets slip the truth about the disguise to Wilfred and is forced to promise him her hand in marriage so that he will not give away her secret.

Hardly has she given her promise when the real Leonard appears with an official pardon for Fairfax. Now Phoebe's father, in order to keep Dame Carruthers from giving away *his* part in the plot, must reluctantly propose marriage to *her* (the plot, in short, has not only thickened; it has become opaque).

Fairfax comes forth, dressed in his own magnificent attire, attended by other gentlemen. He sternly bids Elsie set aside all thoughts of Leonard Meryll and claims her as his bride. Elsie, face averted, submits sorrowfully to her fate, but when she recognizes Fairfax as "Leonard" she is thoroughly delighted.

Phoebe resigns herself to marrying Wilfred in a year—or two—or three at the most, and poor Jack Point, realizing that now Elsie is lost to him forever, falls insensible at her feet.

When Maiden Loves

When Our Gallant Norman Foes

Majestically, but not too slow

DAME CARRUTHERS

1. When our
2. With -

1. gal-lant Nor-man foes Made our mer-ry land their own, And the Sax-ons from the Con-quer-or were
2. in its wall of rock The flow-er of the brave Have

1. fly-ing, At his bid-ding it a-rose, In its pan-o-ply of stone, A
2. per-ished with a con-stan-cy un-shak-en. From the dun-geon to the block, From the scaf-fold to the grave, Is a

sen - ti - nel un - liv - ing and un - dy - ing. In - sen - si - ble, I trow, As a
jour - ney man - y gal - lant hearts have tak - en. And the wick - ed flames may hiss Round the

sen - ti - nel should be, Tho' a queen to save her head should come a - su - ing; There's a
he - roes who have fought For con - science and for home in all its beau - ty; But the

le - gend on its brow That is el - o - quent to me, And it tells of du - ty
grim old for - ta - lice Takes lit - tle heed of aught That comes not in the

rall.   *a tempo*   *p*

done and du - ty do - ing.}   "The screw may twist and the
meas - ure of its du - ty.}

p a tempo

cresc.

rack may turn, And men may bleed and men may burn, O'er Lon - don town and its

f

Is Life a Boon?

Slowly with expression

FAIRFAX

1. Is life a boon? If so, it must be-fall That Death, when-e'er he call, Must call too soon. Though four-score years he give, Yet one would pray to live An-oth-er

2. Is life a thorn? Then count it not a whit! Nay, count it not a whit! Man is well done with it; Soon as he's born He should all means es-say To put the plague a-

moon! What kind of plaint have I,
way; And I, war - worn,

Who per - ish in Ju -
Poor cap - tured fu - gi -

ly, Who per - ish in Ju - ly? I might have had to
tive, My life most glad - ly give, I might have had to

die, Per - chance, in June! I might have had to
live An - oth - er morn!

1.
die, Per - chance, in June!

2.
live, to live An - oth - er morn!

follow the voice

I Have a Song to Sing, O!

sipped no sup, and who craved no crumb, As he sighed for the love of a la - dye!

mp

Heigh - dy! heigh - dy! Mis - er - y me, lack - a - day - dee! He

sipped no sup, and he craved no crumb, As he sighed for the love of a la - dye!

mp POINT

3. I have a song to sing, O!

mf ELSIE   POINT

Sing me your song, O! _____ It is

song of the mer-ry-maid, once so gay, Who turned on her heel and tripped a-way From the

pea-cock pop-in-jay, brave-ly born, Who turned up his no-ble nose with scorn At the

hum-ble heart that he did not prize; So she begged on her knees, with down-cast eyes, For the

love of the mer-ry-man, mop-ing mum, Whose soul was sad and whose glance was glum, Who

sipped no sup, and who craved no crumb, As he sighed for the love of a la-dye!

Heigh - dy! heigh - dy! Mis - er - y me, lack - a - day - dee! His pains were o'er, and he sighed no more, For he lived in the love of a la - dye!

Heigh - dy! heigh - dy! Mis - er - y me, lack - a - day - dee! His pains were o'er, and he sighed no more, For he lived in the love of a la - dye!

Were I Thy Bride

Gracefully

PHOEBE

Were I thy bride, Then all the world be-side Were not too wide To hold my wealth of love, Were I thy bride!

Up-on thy breast My lov-ing head would rest, As on her

nest The ten-der tur-tle dove, Were I thy bride!

This heart of mine Would be one heart with

thine, And in that shrine Our hap-pi-ness would dwell, Were I thy

bride! And all day long Our

lives should be a song: No grief, no wrong Should make my heart re-bel, Were

Were I thy bride! The ro - se's sigh Were as a car-rion's cry To lull-a - by Such as I'd sing to thee, Were I thy bride! A feath - er's press Were lead - en heav-i - ness To my ca - ress. But then, of course, you see, I'm not thy bride!

Oh, a Private Buffoon

Quick but not hurriedly

POINT

1. Oh, a
2. If you
3. If your
4. Comes a
5. Tho' your

pri-vate buf-foon is a light-heart-ed loon, If you lis-ten to pop-u-lar
wish to suc-ceed as a jest-er, you'll need To con-sid-er each per-son's au-
mas-ter is sur-ly, from get-ting up ear-ly (And tem-pers are short in the
Bish-op, may-be, or a sol-emn D. D. Oh, be-ware of his an-ger pro-
head it may rack with a bil-ious at-tack, And your sen-ses with tooth-ache you're

ru-mour; From the morn to the night he's so
ric-'lar: What is all right for B would so quite
morn-ing), An in-op-por-tune joke is e-
vok-ing! Bet-ter not pull his hair, don't stick
los-ing, Don't be mo-py and flat, they don't

joy-ous and bright, And he bub-bles with wit and good
scan-dal-ize C (For C is so ver-y par-
nough to pro-voke Him to give you, at once, a month's
pins in his chair; He don't un-der-stand prac-ti-cal
fine you for that, If you're prop-er-ly quaint and a-

hu - mour! He's so quaint and so terse, both in
tic - 'lar!); And D may be dull, and E's
warn - ing. Then if you re - frain, he is
jok - ing. If the jests that you crack have an
mus - ing! Tho' your wife ran a - way with a

prose and in verse; Yet though peo - ple for - give his trans -
ver - y thick skull Is as emp - ty of brains as a
at you a - gain, For he likes to get val - ue for
or - tho - dox smack, You may get a bland smile from these
sol - dier that day, And took with her your tri - fle of

gres - sion, There are one or two rules that all
la - dle; While F is F sharp, and will
mon - ey; He'll ask then and there, with an
sag - es; But should they, by chance, be im -
mon - ey; Bless your heart, they don't mind, they're ex -

fam - i - ly fools Must ob - serve, if they love their pro -
cry with a carp That he's known your best joke from his
in - so - lent stare, "If you know that you're paid to be
port - ed from France, Half - a - crown is stopp'd out of your
ceed - ing - ly kind, They don't blame you, as long as you're

fes - sion! There are one or two rules, Half - a -
cra - dle! When your hu - mour they flout, You can't
fun - ny?" It adds to the task Of a
wag - es! It's a gen - er - al rule, Tho' your
fun - ny! It's a com - fort to feel, If your

doz - en, may be, That all fam - i - ly fools, Of what -
let your - self go; And it does put you out When a
mer - ry - man's place, When your prin - ci - pal asks, With a
zeal it may quench, If the fam - i - ly fool Tells a
part - ner should flit, Tho' you suf - fer a deal, They don't

ev - er de - gree, Must ob - serve, if they love their pro -
per - son says: "Oh, I have known that old joke from my
scowl on his face, If you know that you're paid to be
joke that's too French, Half - a - crown is stopp'd out of his
mind it a bit; They don't blame you, so long as you're

1.-2.-3.-4.
fes - sion!
cra - dle!"
fun - ny?
wag - es!

5.

fun - ny!

[341]

Strange Adventure

Lightly as a Gavotte

f **KATE**

1. Strange ad - ven - ture! Maid - en wed - ded To a
2. Strange ad - ven - ture that we're troll - ing: Mod - est

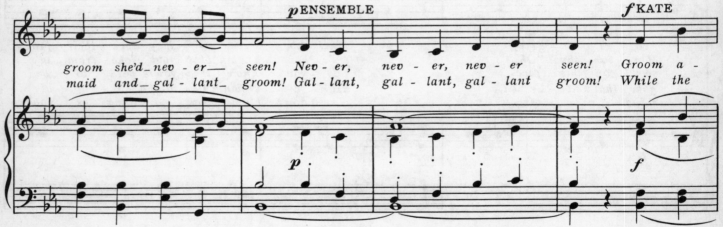

p **ENSEMBLE**   *f* **KATE**

groom she'd_ nev - er_ seen! Nev - er, nev - er, nev - er seen! Groom a -
maid and_ gal - lant_ groom! Gal - lant, gal - lant, gal - lant groom! While the

ENSEMBLE

bout_ to be be - head - ed, In an_ hour on Tow - er Green! Tow - er,
fun - 'ral bell is toll - ing, Toll - ing,_ toll - ing, Bim - a - boom! Bim - a,

mp

[342]

KATE

Tow - er, Tow - er Green! Groom in drear - y — dun - geon ly - ing, Groom as
Bim - a, Bim - a - boom! Mod - est maid - en — will not tar - ry; Though but

good as — dead, or dy - ing, For a pret - ty maid - en sigh - ing, Pret - ty
six - teen — year she car - ry, She must mar - ry, she must mar - ry, Though the

maid of — sev - en - teen! Sev - en, sev - en, — sev - en - teen!
al - tar — be a tomb, Tow - er, Tow - er, — Tow - er

2. *p*ALL

tomb! Tow - er tomb! Tow - er

cresc. *dim. e rall.*

tomb! Though the al - tar be a tomb! Tow - er, Tow - er, — Tow - er tomb!

A Man Who Would Woo a Fair Maid

all may at-tain if they will:___ But ev-er-y Jack, He must

stud-y the knack If he wants to make sure of his Jill! If he

wants to make sure___ of his Jill!

Elsie 2. If he's   Then a

glance may be tim-id or free,___ It will var-y in might-y de-gree,___ From an

When a Wooer Goes A-Wooing

In an easy flowing movement

ELSIE: When a woo-er Goes a-woo-ing, Naught is tru-er Than his joy.

FAIRFAX: Maid-en hush-ing All his su-ing, Bold-ly blush-ing, Brave-ly coy!

ELSIE: Bold-ly blush-ing, Brave-ly coy!

Oh, the hap-py days of do-ing! Oh, the sigh-ing and the su-ing! When a

woo-er goes a-woo-ing, Oh, the sweets that nev - er cloy! When a

broth-er leaves his sis-ter For an-oth-er, Sis-ter weeps. Tears that

trick-le, Tears that blis-ter, 'Tis but mick-le sis-ter reaps! Tears that

trick - - le, Tears that blis - ter.

ELSIE

Oh, the do-ing and un-do-ing, Oh, the sigh-ing and the

su - ing, When a broth-er goes a - woo-ing, And a sob-bing sis - ter

weeps! When a jest-er Is out-wit-ted, Feel-ings fes-ter, Heart is

lead! Food for fish-es On-ly fit-ted, Jest-er wish-es He was

dead! Food for fish-es On-ly fit-ted, Jest-er wish-es He was

dead!_____ Oh, the do-ing and un-do-ing, Oh, the sigh-ing and the

THE GONDOLIERS

OR

The King of Barataria

THE GONDOLIERS

OR
The King of Barataria

SLOWLY but inexorably, the breach between Gilbert and Sullivan was widening. Their relationship is still unique in the field of collaboration, in that two men whose minds could meet and interlock so perfectly, when it came to their joint work, could be so utterly apart in temperament and inclination. Sullivan was gregarious and "social." His intimates were, for the most part, people of title or social importance, with very few musicians among them. If he spent so much of his leisure abroad, at fashionable watering places, it was not entirely for his health. Gilbert, on the other hand, had no use for "society." Like every Englishman of his professional standing, he was a club man; but he managed to keep on generally bad terms with most of his fellow members. His real intimates, what few there were, came from the world in which he did his work. He was, first and last, a man of the theater. Significantly enough, when the final break came, it was the cranky Gilbert, not the suave and courteous Sullivan, with whom the actors sided. Gilbert might be a martinet; he might drill them mercilessly, insist on iron discipline, meddle with their private lives and conduct. Nevertheless, he was one of them, understood them, and, fundamentally, sympathized with them. Sullivan, on the other hand, once he had played over the music at the first reading rehearsal, vanished until it was time for him to conduct the orchestral rehearsals and the opening performance. They neither liked nor disliked him. Simply, he was not one of them, and they knew it.

The signs of serious friction appeared during the run of *The Yeomen*. Gilbert seems to have grown to dislike and distrust D'Oyly Carte, for in reply to someone who had remarked upon the felicity of his partnership with Sullivan, he observed that never, under Carte's management, would he collaborate with Sullivan again. The latter's grievances were not with the management, but with his collaborator. He spoke openly of "this slavery," meaning the necessity for accommodating his music to the rhythms of Gilbert's lyrics. When Gilbert called on him, in January, 1889, to discuss the possibilities of a new opera, he began to list his complaints before Gilbert could open his mouth. *The Yeomen of the Guard*, his most ambitious score to date, had been only a moderate success; nevertheless, he seems to have taken this as a sign for him to go on to bigger and better things—"better" meaning more pretentious. Incidentally, Carte, who had also acquired delusions of grandeur, had conceived the idea of founding an all-English grand-opera company, to produce works by British composers, and had actually bought land and started construction on the opera house that was to be the scene of these productions. When he suggested that Sullivan write the opera that should inaugurate the new venture, the latter naturally jumped at it. Here was the chance he had been looking for, the chance that all his friends, even the Queen herself, had been urging him to take.

In that January interview he cited all this, and suggested that Gilbert write the libretto for him. It is hard to believe that, knowing Gilbert's views on getting out of the field that had been so profitable for them both, he was entirely sincere in this offer. At all events, he made it, and Gilbert was so thunderstruck that he half agreed to undertake the job.

Later, thinking things over, he changed his mind. He thought the site of the new opera house was unsuitable, he was skeptical of Sullivan's being able to assemble a cast that would do dramatic justice to the piece—"Where, in God's name, is your grand-opera soprano who can act be found?"—and, above all, he felt himself unfitted to write a serious libretto; even if he did so, the public would not accept it, coming from him. If Sullivan must have a librettist, he suggested that he take Julian Sturgis, who could turn out the sort of thing he wanted (Sullivan did take him, by the way).

All this he embodied in a letter to Sullivan, who was, as usual, in Monte Carlo. But, he continued, why not both? Why not write a grand opera with Sturgis and a new Savoy opera with him?

Sullivan's reply was to the effect that, nevertheless, he was tired of doing the same old thing, that his music was being wasted on trivial plots, and that he had been subordinating himself to the librettist in every one of their operas. Gilbert wrote back that if Sullivan had really been subordinating himself for twelve years, and now expected him to subordinate *him*self, it was just too bad (those were his sentiments, if not his exact words). "If we meet, it must be as master and master."

Whereupon Sullivan blew up—in a letter, not to Gilbert, but to Carte. Gilbert had always ignored him, had always had a contempt for his opinions—he wasted the company's time in rehearsals, he ruined the music, he tired out the actors, so that they sang off pitch, he was rude, egotistic, and domineering—in short, he was not a lovable type. No sooner had the letter been posted than Sullivan, apparently, regretted it; for he immediately mailed one to Gilbert, mild, almost apologetic in tone, merely saying that he would like to have some say as to the musical construction of their next opus. Unfortunately, Carte (possibly by design) forwarded Sullivan's first letter, so that Gilbert received both by the same mail.

Then followed an interchange of fiery epistles in which each partner relieved his pent-up emotions regarding the other. At last, having blown off steam, they met one evening at Mrs. Ronalds' house (she well knew the value of the association to each of them), talked things over, and shook hands. Soon after, Gilbert sent Sullivan his sketch for the new piece, which the latter thought "funny and pretty," and they went to work.

All was not entirely well with the company, however. In August, George Grossmith left to give all his time to his pianologues. Gilbert begged him to stay, but the act, "Piano and I," was going so well at private parties (owing largely, of course, to the prestige of Grossmith's twelve years of Gilbert and Sullivan) that he insisted on re-embarking on his old career of drawing-room entertainer. He was replaced, in turn, by John Wilkinson and Frank Wyatt. Then Jessie Bond struck for a raise. She felt that her contribution to the operas was worth something more than she was getting —in short, that she ought to have one hundred and fifty dollars a week instead of one hundred. Gilbert, horrified, argued with her, but in vain. (The leading ingenue of a musical comedy today commands at least five hundred a week.) He finally gave in, but warned everybody in sight that there would be no stars in the forthcoming new work. Every role would have a counterpart. Such, eventually, proved to be the case. Even the lead, in the new piece, was assigned to twin brothers!

Sullivan, meanwhile, waited until the last possible minute and then, in November, went furiously to work. On the evening of December 7, 1889, *The Gondoliers; or, The King of Barataria,* opened at the Savoy with this cast:

The Duke of Plaza-Toro	Giorgio ....Mr. de Pledge
Frank Wyatt	Annibale ...... Mr. Wilbraham
Luiz .... Wallace Brownlow	The Duchess of Plaza-Toro
Don Alhambra del Bolero	Rosina Brandram
W. H. Denny	Casilda .... Decima Moore
Marco Palmieri	Gianetta ......Geraldine Ulmar
Courtice Pounds	Tessa .... Jessie Bond
Giuseppe Palmieri	Fiametta .... Miss Lawrence
Rutland Barrington*	Vittoria .... Miss Cole
Antonio .... Mr. Metcalf	Giulia .... Miss Phyllis
Francesco ....Mr. Rose	Inez ... . Miss Bernard

* Back, much sadder and wiser, after his ill-fated excursion into producing.

With the possible exception of *The Mikado*, the opening night of *The Gondoliers* was the greatest triumph of their joint careers. Gilbert had given Sullivan exactly the thing he had said he wanted, i.e., a story that offered musical situations; and Sullivan had obliged with a score of superb spontaneity and tunefulness. It is the gayest of all their operas, and the pity is that it is not heard more often. Gilbert, writing to Sullivan after the opening, said: "It gives one the chance of shining right through the twentieth century with reflected light."

To which Sullivan responded: "Don't talk of reflected light. In such a perfect book as *The Gondoliers* you shine with an individual brilliancy which no other writer can hope to attain."

If only they had kept on believing that!

THE STORY

ACT I

On the Piazetta in Venice, four-and-twenty flower girls are hopefully tying bouquets of ROSES WHITE AND ROSES RED. They plan to present them to Marco and Giuseppe, handsomest of all the gondolieri, objects of every girl's adoration.

Marco and Giuseppe, arriving with their usual dash, declaim with pride, WE'RE CALLED GONDOLIERI. They have come to choose their brides, but feel it would be indelicate to betray partiality by choosing openly. They therefore decide to bestow the privilege on those two girls whom they catch in a game of blindman's buff. By happy chance, Marco catches

Gianetta, and Giuseppe, Tessa—the very girls they wanted.

As all four hurry off to the altar, a gondola draws up, containing the proud but penniless Duke of Plaza-Toro, His Grace's Duchess true, His Grace's daughter, too (Casilda by name), and their "suite," which consists solely of a drummer called Luiz, who happens to be Casilda's secret love. The Duke informs his daughter that when she was a baby she was married by proxy to the infant son of the King of Barataria, who in turn was kidnaped by the Grand Inquisitor for political reasons. They have come to Venice, the Duke reveals, to find the missing heir and hail Casilda as Queen. To help raise enough money for the venture, the Duke has incorporated himself as a commercial enterprise to be known as the Duke of Plaza-Toro, Limited. He expects to do quite as well in commerce as he did IN ENTERPRISE OF MARTIAL KIND.

Casilda and Luiz have barely a moment to lament the fact that THERE WAS A TIME when they were far happier when Don Alhambra, the Grand Inquisitor, appears and explains how I STOLE THE PRINCE. This full confession makes it clear that the prince was placed in the home of a highly respectable gondolier who had a child of the same age. Unfortunately, because of a taste for tippling, the gondolier perished, and no one knows which of his two heirs is the royal stripling.

At this moment, Marco and Giuseppe and their two pretty brides return from their wedding, full of the joy that tarries WHEN A MERRY MAIDEN MARRIES. The Grand Inquisitor, positive that one of them—although he doesn't know which—is the lost King, persuades them to return with him to Barataria. He adjures them to forget their republican principles, to desert their brides for the moment, and reign as joint monarchs until he can ascertain from the King's ancient nurse (who is the mother of Luiz, a fact which the reader had better remember) which is which. The gondoliers and their brides consent on the condition that they may have a truly democratic court. The brides tell their husbands, O MY DARLING, O MY PET, whatever else you may forget, do not forget you've married me. After a tearful farewell, Marco and Giuseppe leave for Barataria.

ACT II

In a pavilion in the Court of Barataria, Marco and Giuseppe are cleaning the crown and scepter, clad in their kingly robes, while the servants and assorted ministers of state are chatting and indulging in games of chance, without reference to social distinction. The two monarchs believe in complete equality. They feel that men who hold the magnificent privilege of heading the subscription lists of all principal charities should do something to justify themselves. They explain how, RISING EARLY IN THE MORNING, they work busily all day for their subjects. The only cloud on their joint horizons is the absence of their wives, for, as Marco counsels Giuseppe, the only recipe for perfect happiness is to TAKE A PAIR OF SPARKLING EYES, add a figure trimly planned, and everything that goes with it.

Just then the two girls arrive, unable to bear separation any longer, and their overjoyed husbands and the entire court DANCE A CACHUCHA. They are interrupted by the unexpected appearance of the Grand Inquisitor, who is shocked and pained at the court's promiscuous democracy. He warns them that THERE LIVED A KING in days of old who tried this sort of thing with unhappy results; since, obviously, when everybody's somebody, then no one's anybody. He breaks the news that whichever of the gondoliers is King will have to marry Casilda. This somewhat depresses everyone, since it is clear that the married couples are confronted with the problem of two men married to three women. Chaos results, which is interrupted by the entrance of the Duke, the Duchess, Casilda, and their "suite," Luiz. The two brides commiserate with Casilda on her rather vague wedded state. The Duke of Plaza-Toro, sharing the Grand Inquisitor's disappointment of the court's informality, instructs the two kings in royal dignity and the proper method of behaving when I AM A COURTIER GRAVE AND SERIOUS.

But just as the gondoliers and their three bewildered brides are wondering who is who, the Inquisitor returns with the King's old nurse, Inez, whom he has been tactfully questioning in the torture chamber. Inez explains that when the Inquisitor came to kidnap the royal babe, she tricked him by substituting her own son and raised the King as her child. So the King of Barataria is—of all people—Luiz, the Duke's "suite." The two gondoliers are really gondoliers. Casilda, who has loved Luiz in secret, can—in fact, must—now marry him, and Giuseppe and Marco return with their brides to the republican life of their chosen profession.

Roses White and Roses Red

Moderately bright CHORUS of GIRLS

List and learn, list and

learn, List and learn, ye dain- ty ros- es, Ros- es

white and ros- es red, Why we bind you in - to po- sies Ere_ your morn-ing bloom has

fled. By a law of maid- en's mak- ing, Ac- cents of— a heart that's ach- ing, E- ven

red, Why we bind you in-to po-sies Ere_ your morn-ing bloom_ has

fled. List and learn, list and learn, Ros-es white and ros-es

red, Ros - - - es, oh list, list _ and

learn, List _ and learn, _____ Oh, ros-es white_ and

red! _____

We're Called Gondolieri

In lively, very spirited tempo

MARCO and GIUSEPPE

We're called _____ gon-do-lier-i, But that's a va-ga-ry,_ It's_ quite hon-or - a-ry_ The_ trade that_ we_ ply._

For gal - - lant-ry not-ed Since we were short coat-ed,_ To_ beau-ty_ de-

la, Our— man - do - lins— tun-ing, We— la - zi-ly

thrum.Tra-la-la-la - la-la-la,Tra-la-la-la - la-la - la,Tra-la-la-la - la,Tra-la-la-la-

la!————— When ves - pers are ring-ing, To hope ev-er cling-ing,—With—

songs of— our— sing-ing— A— vig-il we— keep.————————

When day-light is fad - ing, En-wrapt in night's

shad - ing, With soft ser - e - nad - ing,

We sing them to sleep, _____

With soft _____ ser - - - - -

- e - nad - - - - - ing We sing them to

sleep, _____ With soft ser - e - nad-ing We sing them to

sleep.   We're called gon - do - lier - i,   But ___

that's a _____ va - ga - ry.   Gon - do - lier - i,   gon - do -

lier - i, Tra - la - la - la - la,   Tra - la - la - la - la - la!   Gon - do -

lier - i,   gon - do - lier - i, Tra - la - la - la - la, Tra - la - la - la - la, Tra - la - la - la -

la, Tra - la - la - la - la, Tra - la - la - la - la!   Tra - la! ___

[365]

In Enterprise of Martial Kind

Bright martial tempo

DUKE

1. In _ en-ter-prise of mar-tial kind, When there was an-y _ fight-ing, He _ led his reg'-ment from be-hind, He found it less _ ex-cit-ing. But _ when a-way his reg'-ment ran, His place was at the fore, O! That

2. When, to e-vade De-struc-tion's hand, To hide they all _ pro-ceed-ed, No _ sol-dier in that gal-lant band Hid half as well as _ he did. He _ lay con-ceal'd through-out the war, And so pre-serv'd his gore, O! That

3. When told that they would all be shot Un-less they left _ the _ ser-vice, That he-ro hes-i-tat-ed not, So mar-vel-lous _ his nerve is. He _ sent his re-sig-na-tion in, The first of _ all his corps, O! That

There Was a Time

me, ah, woe is me! Casilda (upper) Luiz (lower) Oh, bur-y, bur-y, let the grave close o'er The

days that were, that nev-er will be more! Oh, bur-y, bur-y love that all con-

demn, And let the whirl-wind_ mourn_ its_ re-qui-em!

CASILDA
Dead as the last year's leaves, As gath-er'd flow'rs, ah, woe is me!

Dead as the gar-ner'd sheaves, That love of ours, ah, woe is me! Born but to fade and

I Stole the Prince

Brightly, but not too fast

DON ALHAMBRA

1. I
2. But
3. Time
4. The

stole the Prince, and I brought him here, And left him gai - ly
ow - ing, I'm much dis - posed to fear, To his ter - ri - ble taste for
sped, and when at the end of a year, I sought that in - fant
chil - dren fol - lowed his old ca - reer (This state - ment can't be

prat - tling With a high - ly re - spect - a - ble gon - do - lier, Who
tip - pling, That high - ly re - spect - a - ble gon - do - lier Could
cher - ished, That high - ly re - spect - a - ble gon - do - lier Was
par - ried) Of a high - ly re - spect - a - ble gon - do - lier: Well,

prom-ised the Roy - al babe to rear, And teach him the trade of a
nev - er de - clare with a mind sin - cere Which of the two was his
ly - ing a corpse on his hum - ble bier, I dropp'd a Grand In -
one of the two (who will soon be here), But which of the two it is

ti - mon - eer With his own be - lov - ed brat - ling.
off - spring dear,— And which the Roy - al strip - ling!
quis - i - tor's tear,— That gon - do - lier had per - ished!
not quite clear, Is the Roy - al Prince you mar - ried! A Search

Both of the babes were strong and stout, And, con - sid - er - ing all things,
Which was which he could nev - er make out De - spite his best en -
taste for drink, com - bined— with gout, Had dou - bled him up for -
in and out and round— a - bout And you'll dis - cov - er

clev - er. Of that there is no man - ner of doubt, No
deav - our. Of that there is no man - ner of doubt, No
ev - er. Of that there is no man - ner of doubt, No
nev - er A tale so free from ev - er - y doubt, All

prob - a - ble, pos - si - ble sha - dow of doubt, No pos - si - ble doubt what-
prob - a - ble, pos - si - ble sha - dow of doubt, No pos - si - ble doubt what-
prob - a - ble, pos - si - ble sha - dow of doubt, No pos - si - ble doubt what-
prob - a - ble, pos - si - ble sha - dow of doubt, All pos - si - ble doubt what-

1.-2.-3. DUCHESS and CASILDA

ev - er. No pos - si - ble doubt what - ev - er!
ev - er. No pos - si - ble doubt what - ev - er!
ev - er. No pos - si - ble doubt what - ev - er!

4.

ev - er. A tale so free from ev - 'ry doubt, All prob - a - ble, pos - si - ble

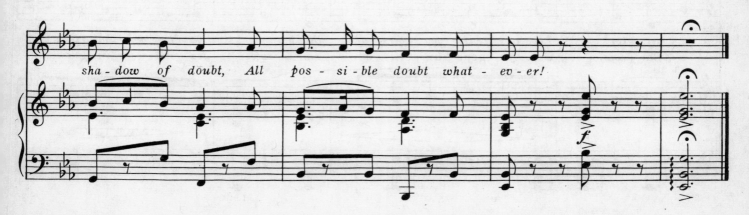

sha - dow of doubt, All pos - si - ble doubt what - ev - er!

When a Merry Maiden Marries

In light and graceful tempo

TESSA

1. When a mer-ry maid-en
2. When a mer-ry maid-en

mar - ries, Sor - row goes and pleas - ure tar - ries; Ev - 'ry sound be - comes a
mar - ries, Sor - row goes and pleas - ure tar - ries; Ev - 'ry sound be - comes a

song, All is right and noth - ing's wrong! From to - day and ev - er
song, All is right and noth - ing's wrong! Gnaw - ing Care and ach - ing

af - ter Let our tears be tears of laugh - ter, Ev - 'ry sigh that finds a
Sor - row, Get ye gone un - til to - mor - row; Jeal - ous - ies in grim ar -

O My Darling, O My Pet

Slowly, but not dragging

GIANETTA

Now, Mar-co dear, My wish-es hear: While you're a-way It's un-der-stood You will be good, And not too gay.

To ev-'ry trace Of maid-en grace You will be blind, And will not glance by an-y chance On wo-man-kind!

If you are wise, You'll shut your eyes Till we ar-rive, And not ad-dress A la-dy less Than for-ty-five.

You'll please to frown On ev'ry gown That you may see; And, O my pet, You won't for-get You've mar-ried me!

cresc.

p

mf

And, O my dar-ling, O my pet, What-ev-er else you may for-

mf espressivo

get, In yon-der isle be-yond the sea, Do not for-get, Do not for-get You've mar-ried me! You'll

TESSA
p

p

lay your head Up-on your bed At set of sun. You will not sing Of an-y-thing To an-y-one. You'll

GIANETTA

sea, Do not for - get You've mar - ried me! O __ my dar - ling, O my

pet, What - ev - er else you may for - get, In yon - der isle be - yond the sea, Do not for -

get, Do not for - get You've mar - ried me! O __ my

dar - ling, O my pet, In yon - der isle be - yond the

sea, Do not for - get You've mar - ried me! __

[380]

Rising Early in the Morning

du-ty, he's a touch-y lit-tle man),Write some let-ters lit-er - a-ry For our pri-vate sec - re-
tith-er, up and down and to and fro, While the war-ri - or on du-ty Goes in search of beer and

ta-ry: He is shak-y in his spell-ing, so we help him if we can. Then, in
beau-ty (And it gen-er-al-ly hap-pens that he has-n't far to go). He re-

view of crav-ings in-ner, We go down and or-der din-ner; Then we pol-ish the Re-ga-lia and the
lieves us, if he's a-ble, Just in time to lay the ta-ble, Then we dine and serve the cof-fee, and at

Cor-o - na-tion plate, Spend an hour in tit-i - vat-ing All our Gen-tle-men- in-Wait-ing; Or we
half-past twelve or one, With a pleas-ure that's em-phat-ic, We re - ti - re to our at - tic With the

run on lit - tle er-rands for the Min-is-ters of State. Oh,— phi-los-o-phers may sing Of the
grat-i - fy-ing feel-ing that our du-ty has been done! Oh,— phi-los-o-phers may sing Of the

trou - bles of a King; Yet the du - ties are de - light - ful, and the
trou - bles of a King; But of pleas - ures there are man - y and of

priv - i - leg - es great; But the priv - i - lege and pleas - ure That we
wor - ries there are none; And the cul - mi - nat - ing pleas - ure That we

treas - ure be - yond meas - ure Is to run on lit - tle er - rands for the
treas - ure be - yond meas - ure Is the grat - i - fy - ing feel - ing that our

1.
Min - is - ters of State. Af - ter du - ty has been

2. rit

done!

Take a Pair of Sparkling Eyes

Moderately and with warmth

MARCO

1. Take a pair of spark - ling eyes,___ Hid - den, ev - er and a -
2. Take a pret - ty lit - tle cot,___ Quite a min - ia - ture af -

non,___ In a mer - ci - ful e - clipse.___ Do not
fair,___ Hung a - bout with trel - liss'd vine, ___ Fur - nish

heed their mild sur - prise,___ Hav - ing pass'd the Ru - bi - con.___ Take a
it up - on the spot___ With the trea - sures rich and rare___ I've en -

pair of ros - y lips; _____ Take a fig - ure trim - ly
deav - our'd to _ de - fine. _____ Live to love and love to

plann'd, Such as ad - mi - ra - tion whets _ (Be par - tic - u - lar in
live, _ You will rip - en at your ease, _ Grow - ing on the sun - ny

this); Take a ten - der lit - tle hand, _ Fring'd with dain - ty fin - ger-
side. Fate has noth - ing more to give. _ You're a dain - ty man to

ettes, _ Press _____ it, press it in pa - ren - the -
please, If _____ you're not sat - is - fied, not _ sat - is -

Take my coun - sel, hap - py man;

Act up - on it, if you can, if you

can, if you can, Act up - on it, if you can,_____ hap - py

man, if___ you can!_____

Dance a Cachucha

Brilliantly and gaily

mf CHORUS

Dance a — ca - chu - cha, fan - dan - go, bo - le - ro, Xe - res — we'll —
drink, Man - za - nil - la, Mon - te - ro, Wine, when — it — runs in a —

bun - dance, en - hanc - es The reck - less de - light of that wild - est of

danc - es! To the pret - ty pit - ter, pit - ter, pat - ter, And the clit - ter, clit - ter, clit - ter,

clat - ter, Clit - ter, clit - ter, clat - ter, Pit - ter, pit - ter, pat - ter, Clit - ter, clit - ter, clat - ter,

clit - ter, clit - ter, To the pret - ty pit - ter, pit - ter, pat - ter, And the clit - ter, clit - ter, clit - ter,

clat - ter, Pit - ter, pit - ter, pit - ter, pat - ter, pat - ter, pat - ter, pat - ter, We'll

dance, Old Xe - res we'll drink, Man - za - nil - la, Mon - te - ro, For wine, when it

f

marcato

sempre marcato

runs in a - bun-dance, en - hanc - es The reck - less de - light of that

wild - est of danc - es, that wild - est of danc - es, The reck - less de - light! ____

mf

Dance a ca - chu - cha, fan - dan - go, bo - le - ro, Xe - res_ we'll

mf

drink, Man - za - nil - la, Mon - te - ro, Wine, when it_ runs in a - bun - dance, en -

There Lived a King

Brightly, but not too fast

DON ALHAMBRA

There lived a King, as I've been told, In the won-der-work-ing days of old, When hearts were twice as good as gold, And twen-ty times_ as_ mel-low. Good tem-per tri-umphed in_ his_ face, And in his heart he found a_ place For

So to the top of ev-'ry tree Pro-mot-ed ev-'ry-bod-y. Now

and GIUSEPPE

that's the kind of King for me, He wished all men as rich as he,

So to the top of ev-'ry tree Pro-mot-ed ev-'ry-bod-y! Lord

ALHAMBRA

Chan-cel-lors were cheap as sprats, And Bish-ops in their shov-el hats Were
King, al-though no one de-nies His heart was of ab-nor-mal size, Yet

plen-ti-ful as tab-by cats, In point of fact,_ too_ man-y. Am-
he'd have act-ed oth-er-wise If he had been_ a_ cut-er. The

bas - sa - dors cropped up_ like_ hay, Prime Min - is - ters and such_ as_ they Grew
end is eas - i - ly_ fore-told, When ev -'ry bless - ed thing you_ hold Is

like as - par - a - gus in May, And Dukes were_ three a pen - ny. On_
made of sil - ver, or of gold, You long for_ sim - ple pew - ter. When

ev -'ry side Field Mar - shals gleam'd, Small beer were Lords Lieu - ten - ant deem'd, With
you have noth - ing else to wear But cloth of gold and sat - ins rare, For

MARCO
Ad - mi - rals the o - cean teem'd, All round his wide do - min - ions. With
cloth of_ gold you cease to care, Up goes the price of shod - dy. Of

and GIUSEPPE
DON ALHAMBRA
Ad - - - mi - rals a - round his_ wide do - min - ions. And
shod - - - dy, up goes_ the_ price of shod - dy. In

Par - ty Lead - ers you might meet In twos and threes in ev - 'ry street, Main-
short, who - ev - er you may be, To this con - clu - sion you'll a - gree, When

MARCO

tain - ing,— with no— lit - tle heat, Their var - i - ous o - pin - ions. Now
ev - 'ry - one is— some - bod - ee, Then no one's an - y - bod - y! Now

and GIUSEPPE

that's a sight you could - n't beat, Two Par - ty Lead - ers in each street Main-
that's as plain as plain can be, To this con - clu - sion we a - gree, When

1. DON

tain - ing,— with no— lit - tle heat, Their var - i - ous o - pin - ions! That
ev - 'ry - one is— some - bod - ee, Then no one's an - y -

2.

bod - y!

[397]

I Am a Courtier Grave and Serious

Slowly like a Gavotte

p DUKE

1. I— am a cour-tier grave and ser-ious Who— is a-
bout to kiss your hand: Try— to com-bine a pose im-per-ious With— a de-

MARCO and GIUSEPPE

mean- our no-bly bland. Let us com-bine a pose im-per-ious With a de-

bend - ing; Off— we — go to the oth - er ex - treme, Too— con -

found-ed - ly— con - de - scend-ing!

DUKE

2. Now— a ga-

votte per - form se - date-ly, Of - fer your hand with con - scious

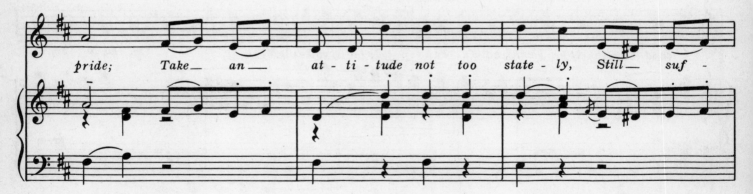

pride; Take— an — at - ti - tude not too state - ly, Still— suf -

MARCO and GIUSEPPE

fi - cient-ly dig - ni - fied. Now for an at - ti - tude not too

state - ly, Still suf - fi - cient - ly dig - ni - fied! Once - ly, twice - ly, once - ly,

twice - ly, Bow im - pres - sive - ly ___ ere you glide. Cap - i - tal, both,

cap - i - tal, both, you've caught it nice - ly! That is the style of ___ thing pre -

CASILDA and DUCHESS

cise - ly! Cap - i - tal, both, cap - i - tal, both, you've caught it nice - ly! That is the

MARCO and GIUSEPPE

style of ___ thing pre - cise - ly! Oh, sweet to earn a no - ble - man's

praise! Cap-i-tal, both, cap-i-tal, both, we've caught it nice-ly! Sup-pos-ing he's

right in what he says, This is the style of thing pre-

CASILDA and DUCHESS

cise-ly! Cap-i-tal, both, cap-i-tal, both, you've caught it nice-ly! That is the

style of thing pre-cise-ly! That is the style of thing, the style

of thing pre-cise-ly!

EPILOGUE

It was in August, 1890, with *The Gondoliers* running happily, that the London public rubbed its collective eyes in bewilderment to read in the papers that Mr. W. S. Gilbert had applied for a receiver at the Savoy Theatre and was bringing an action against Mr. D'Oyly Carte and Sir Arthur Sullivan. It was the climactic point of the famous carpet quarrel.

After the successful opening of *The Gondoliers*, Sullivan had left for his inevitable Monte Carlo outing, while Gilbert took a trip to India. On his return to London, Carte sent him a statement of the production expenses of *The Gondoliers*. It aggregated what was then the unprecedented sum of about $22,500. When Gilbert demanded an itemized bill, he found that Carte had included a charge of $2500 for new carpets for the theater. Since Carte already had an allowance of $20,000 a year for rent and maintenance of the Savoy, Gilbert felt that he was being asked to share an expense that had nothing to do with the production of *The Gondoliers*; and he said so, in a letter.

Carte's reply was to the effect that he and Sullivan were sick of Gilbert's perpetual interference with matters that did not concern him; that, if it continued, they would have to look for a new librettist. It is hard to avoid the suspicion that the letter was deliberately framed to infuriate Gilbert. At any rate, it did. After all, he had not only supplied the librettos for a world-famous series of operettas; he had also revolutionized stage direction, as applied to musical shows. Furthermore, Carte's offices in the Savoy were also being used as headquarters for his newly formed English Grand Opera Company, of which Gilbert had no part. As he expressed it, in one of several stormy interviews with Carte, "Do you think I'm going to pay for a confounded carpet for the stairs to an office where you do the dirty business of your blasted opera house, you so-and-so?"

This was not, possibly, tactful language. At the same time, it did—and still does—look as if Carte were trying to get rid of Gilbert, and to anger him into doing the resigning. When Sullivan returned, in April, 1890, he and his partner had a meeting at which Gilbert read him a new form of agreement among the three of them. The composer agreed in principle, but later wrote that he didn't consider a new agreement necessary until the time came for a new opera. Gilbert's reply to this was a letter, to both Sullivan and Carte, announcing that there would be no more performances of his librettos after Christmas, 1890, that *The Gondoliers* would be the last of their works to be performed in public.

Carte apparently felt that he had gone too far. He called a meeting of the three, at which Sullivan sided—with Carte. Angered and hurt by what he considered his partner's treachery, Gilbert stormed out of the meeting, and the next day wrote to Sullivan, demanding that he apologize for his attitude and sever all connections with Carte; otherwise, the partnership was dissolved. Sullivan wrote back that Gilbert had not behaved like a gentleman.

The reason for Sullivan's siding with Carte is clear enough. The latter was building an opera house in which he, Sullivan, was to realize his life's ambition of seeing produced there a grand opera of his own composition. How could he afford to let the cost of a new carpet alienate him from Carte at this particular moment? It was not a particularly noble point of view, but it was certainly a human one. On the other hand, Gilbert was not the man to make allowances for it. He brought suit against Sullivan and Carte in August, demanding an accounting. The case was too involved to discuss here. Suffice it to say that Gilbert won a technical victory, and was so pleased by it that he immediately wrote to Sullivan, suggesting that they forget their differences. Sullivan replied that he couldn't consider a reconciliation until Gilbert acknowledged that he was in the wrong. Miraculously enough, Gilbert, after taking two months to cool off, actually did admit that his gout had caused him to lose his temper, and compromised the carpet case with Carte.

But the breach was still there. When Sullivan's long-awaited grand opera, *Ivanhoe*, was produced at the new opera house on January 31, 1891, Gilbert was not there. He did go, however, about two weeks later, and admitted that he hadn't been bored.

Ivanhoe ran for 160 performances, and Sullivan was greatly depressed. He had expected it—Lord knows why—to run as long as a successful Savoy opera. The wonder is that it ran as long as it did. No opera had ever run for 160 consecutive performances before, and none has since — nor ever will, in my belief. Carte's whole scheme — assembling a double company, and opening an opera house, with a repertoire of one opera —was fantastic and doomed from the start. When *Ivanhoe* closed, he put on Messager's *La Basoche* (hardly all-English, that), and finally sold the house to a vaudeville syndicate.

In October, '91, the music publisher, Chappell, worried at the estrangement of the two famous partners, undertook to conduct peace negotiations. He induced them to meet on October 12, when they had a long talk and finally shook hands. The partnership, however, remained as yet dissolved. Gilbert had taken his beloved lozenge plot to Alfred Cellier, who wrote music for it, and had it produced as *The Mountebanks* at the Lyric Theatre on January 4, 1892. The libretto turned out to be surprisingly good, and the piece had a good run. Sullivan, meanwhile, had undertaken to set a libretto by Sidney Grunday and, after nearly dying of an attack of his old ailment, finally succeeded in finishing the score. The result, *Haddon Hall*, was produced by Carte at the Savoy on September 24, 1892, with Gilbert among the first-night audience. Some of the music became popular, but the piece was a comparative failure.

Carte had guessed wrong. He had made the mistake that so many critics and producers have made, of assuming that the music will make a success of a comic opera. It never does. Unless the libretto has genuine theatrical interest, no matter how light in texture, the score will not save it. *The Mountebanks* had a good book, and *Haddon Hall* had not. Gilbert was vindicated.

Carte, being primarily a businessman, was not one to let false pride stand in his way. He made prompt overtures to Gilbert, and by the end of 1892 the pair had agreed to write their next opera together. Gilbert finished the libretto by July, 1893, and Sullivan—remarking, "after all, there's nobody like him"—went happily to work on the music. There was one rift. Sullivan objected to the finale of the second act, and finally Gilbert, in exasperation, told him to go ahead and write the music first; he would fit the words to it afterwards. This was the first time, during all the years of their association, that Sullivan had failed to find music for Gilbert's words. It was an ominous symptom of their fundamental alienation.

Utopia, Limited; or, The Flowers of Progress, was produced at the Savoy on the evening of October 7, 1893, amid scenes of great excitement. At the close of the performance, Gilbert and Sullivan at first took their calls separately, as had been agreed. Suddenly, while Gilbert was bowing at one side of the stage, Sullivan appeared at the other side, his hand outstretched. Gilbert promptly seized it, and the audience cheered. The breach was healed.

But it was not. *Utopia, Limited*, had "rave" notices from the critics, and had a fair success, but ran only a little over 250 performances—a failure, from the Savoy point of view. There was something missing. It was as if the minds of the two, long married, had come together after an estrangement during which each had been unfaithful to the other. The old spark was missing, the complete mutual understanding was gone.

Each went his own way again. Gilbert revamped a discarded libretto of his, got Osmond Carr to write the music, and produced it, as *His Excellency*, in October, '94. In December, Carte produced the old *Contrabandista*, with some rewriting by Burnand and some extra music by Sullivan, as *The Chieftain*.

Finally, toward the end of 1894, Gilbert sent Sullivan a new libretto, which Sullivan set. The halfheartedness with which the old partners were now collaborating was disastrously apparent when *The Grand Duke; or, The Statutory Duel*, was produced at the Savoy on March 7, 1896. It ran only 123 performances, about four months—a failure from any point of view. Each blamed the other for the failure, and they finally parted, never to speak again.

Sullivan still remained comparatively active, despite his constantly failing health. He wrote a ballet for the Queen's Diamond Jubilee in May, 1897, and late in the spring of '98 saw his *The Beauty Stone*, with a libretto by Arthur Pinero, open and close at the Savoy (56 performances). Carte kept the house open with a series of revivals of the old successes, including a gala production of *The Sorcerer*, on November 17, 1898, to celebrate the twenty-first anniversary of its original opening. Sullivan conducted, and he and Gilbert bowed, at the end, from opposite sides of the stage. They did not speak. This was the last time they ever saw each other.

In November, '99, Sullivan had another production, *The Rose of Persia*, with a libretto by Basil Hood, which ran 100 nights. Early in 1900 he went to Berlin, conducted a special performance of *The Mikado*, and met Kaiser Wilhelm II. In August he went to Switzerland, to work on another piece with Hood, *The Emerald Isle*. He was not to complete it. He died in London, on November 21, 1900, at the age of fifty-eight years and six months. Gilbert, who was ill of rheumatic fever in Egypt, knew nothing of his death until he read it in the papers. Carte, too, was ill (he was to die a few months later), too ill to be told of Sullivan's fate. Some premonition, however, dragged him out of bed and to the window in time to see the funeral procession pass along the Thames Embankment. When he was found, lying exhausted on the floor, he murmured, "I have just seen the last of my old friend Sullivan."

Gilbert had retired to his country estate, Grim's Dyke, which he had bought in 1891. Its 110 acres included a house that was a museum of theatrical mementos, a lake, a virtual menagerie of monkeys, dogs, and lemurs, and, of course, an oversize tennis court. In his later years he became a justice of the peace and was a particular terror to motorists—although he himself eventually succumbed and bought, first, a Locomobile (a steamer) and, next, a Rolls-Royce, in both of which he managed to have a few crackups on his own account.

In 1907, Victoria having died, he was knighted by Edward VII. He pooh-poohed the honor, objected to being called a "playwright" instead of a "dramatist"— but accepted. He made a libretto out of his old play, *The Wicked World*, and had it produced as *Fallen Fairies*, with music by Edward German, on September 16, 1909. It was not a success, and he resolved to write no more librettos. His last stage piece was a one-act sketch called *The Hooligan*, produced in 1911.

On May 29, 1911, he motored two young women from the Harrow station to Grim's Dyke, where they had planned a swimming party. The girls went into the water while he was still changing, and one of them got out of her depth. Gilbert heard her calling for help, dived in, reached her, and said, "Put your hands on my shoulders." As she did so, he sank. He was hauled out by one of the gardeners and given artificial respiration, but to no avail. He had died, not of drowning, but of syncope, in his seventy-fifth year.

The last of the Savoyards had gone. "Gilbert and Sullivan" was now a tradition.

ABOUT THE CONTRIBUTING EDITORS

DEEMS TAYLOR is responsible for all of the text in this book other than W. S. Gilbert's lyrics. He was born in New York City in 1885. He is the composer of *Through the Looking Glass*, an orchestral suite that is in the repertoire of virtually every major symphonic organization in America and Europe, and two operas: *The King's Henchman*, with a book by Edna St. Vincent Millay, and *Peter Ibbetson*. He is the author of the best sellers, *Of Men and Music* and *The Well-Tempered Listener*. For six years now he has been commentator for the New York Philharmonic Symphony Orchestra's Sunday-afternoon broadcasts. He is also currently appearing on the screen as commentator for Walt Disney's *Fantasia*.

LUCILLE CORCOS supplied not only the basic conception of this book, but also its entire galaxy of illustrations. She was born in New York City in 1908 and has been a Gilbert-and-Sullivan fan since high-school days, when she designed sets for *H.M.S. Pinafore* and was a sister and a cousin and an aunt. She has exhibited at the Art Institute of Chicago, Whitney Museum, Metropolitan Museum of Art, and other leading United States museums. A one-woman show of her paintings was held on 57th Street last year. Her paintings and drawings have been appearing for years in *Vanity Fair*, *Vogue*, *Harper's Bazaar*, and other magazines.

ALBERT SIRMAY, creator of the piano arrangements, studied piano at the Royal Academy of Music in Budapest. He wrote twelve operettas which were produced in Budapest, Vienna, Berlin, and London. In 1923, in Vienna, he met Max Dreyfus, the dean of American music publishers, who offered Sirmay a position in his publishing house. Sirmay has subsequently become musical advisor and editor to almost a whole generation of young American composers. Sirmay was one of the late George Gershwin's intimate friends. He edited all of Gershwin's compositions starting with the *Rhapsody in Blue* up to and including the score of *Porgy and Bess*.